MASTHEAD

EDITORS	M.Bartley Seigel
	Roxane Gay
ASSOCIATE EDITOR	Brad Green
ASSISTANT EDITORS	Abby Koski
	Jason Sommer
COVER ARTIST	Brandon Bedaw
READERS	Mairead Case
	Sara Crowley
	Brett Elizabeth Jenkins
	Court Merrigan
	Diana Salier
	Eric Shonkwiler
	Joe Stracci
	Robb Todd
	Brandi Wells
	Hedy Zimra

ADVISORY BOARD

Cecil Giscombe
Bob Hicok
Taylor Mali
Michael Martone
Daniel Nester
Amber Tamblyn
Keith Taylor
Kette Thomas
Deb Olin Unferth

www.pankmagazine.com

CONTENTS

1,001 Awesome Words Contest, 2011 Winners

ON THE REJUVENATING EFFECTS OF ARCH THEFT

BEN ROGERS

ABSTRACT

The authors ditch a mechanical engineering conference to partake in tomfoolery. They have a hell of a time, inspiring them to sanction a new conference in order to partake again, on an annual basis. The authors get old. One of them gets pancreatic cancer. The remaining authors are once again inspired, this time to illegally remove a monument from its foundation and transport it across state lines for reasons that may or may not become clear to the reader. Initial data, albeit mostly anecdotal, suggest that this form of treatment creates joy unobtainable with conventional techniques.

BACKGROUND

The first meeting of the American Society of Mechanical Engineers (ASME) convened in New York in 1880. Exactly one century later, the ASME Conference on Education was held in San Francisco, CA. Among the professors in attendance were the authors of this study. These five gentlemen were casually acquainted, having attended many such conferences together, and their camaraderie had increased as a function of time, owing at least in part to their mutual disdain for the ASME annual conference—a gathering characterized by the tameness of the attendees' neckties, the sameness of the conference centers regardless of host city, and the general sobriety pervading the welcoming mixer. Also prevalent in recent years, PowerPoint (see B. Gates et al.) and females.[1]

During a mid-morning break on the second day of the 1980 conference, the authors stepped outside to converse in private (i.e., outside the auditory radius of fellow nerds). Ambient conditions were 63°F with 78% relative humidity and cloudy skies. Such conversations tended toward mockery of one or more the following: (1) the sexuality of certain plenary lecturers, (2) the sordid past of the hotel bedding, (3) one another. In the present case, however, the topic was the sanctioned evening activity: a bus trip to a new, state-of-the-art HVAC control center at Stanford University. Various alternatives to this tour were proposed and debated. Due consideration was given to the fact that the dinner at the campus dining commons would be complementary.

Ginsberg (1956) shows that diversions abound in San Francisco for the best minds of one's generation. His oft-cited work on the topic concludes that such minds are eventually left "destroyed by madness, starving hysterical naked, dragging themselves through the negro streets at dawn, looking for an angry fix." It was an option.

The authors (who shall be referred to here as Berkeley, Irvine, (San) Diego, Cambridge, and Eugene) were willing to

---

[1] By definition only in nearly all cases. Not "ladies," or "women," or "biscuits," mind you. Females.

consider others, and soon made a fateful observation of an incontrovertible fact: the distance from San Francisco to Reno is 218 miles. Further, a rental car averaging 75 mph can cover this distance in under three hours. Prior studies of Reno focus on divorce (see, e.g., A. Miller, 1961) and cowboys (Ibid.). And J. Cash (1956) conducted a well-known experiment there, in which a man was shot so as to observe his death. Of greater relevance in the present case is the city's proximity to the 1980 ASME Annual Conference; specifically, the following relationship:

Eq. (1)   *218 miles > separation needed to ensure zero encounters with ASME attendees*

Also relevant in this case: Reno's deep-rooted association with the field of statistics.[2]

A Pontiac Grand Am was rented in San Francisco at 11 am on Friday, June 27, 1980, and returned at 3:30 pm the following day. Because Reno ≠ Las Vegas, The Code does not apply. What happened in Reno: Diego received a lap dance from a homeless woman, for which he grossly over-tipped; Irvine snuck onto the Circus Circus trapeze between shows and swung naked yet unnoticed in the dark above the bustling midway; Eugene ingested and regurgitated an Awful Awful cheeseburger + accompanying basket of fries + 750 ml of Old Crow (earning him the nickname Old Crow), then ingested an unknown number of Mentos and Rolaids—also regurgitated; Berkeley forded the Truckee River while holding forth on plate fin heat exchangers; Cambridge met an off-shift cocktail waitress at the Club Cal Neva sports book, with whom he later determined the suspension limits of a parked Subaru Justy.

In this initial assessment of the city, it was found that the equation balanced: Reno took the authors' money, and gave back the 28.5 most liberating hours of their careers.

Our careers. We—the authors.

We were assistant professors. We spent our days slogging through bureaucracy, writing 50-page proposals doomed to go unfunded, spoon-feeding thesis hints to grad students, lecturing to the stoned, and stepping gingerly among the political landmines of our respective mechanical engineering departments. We spent our evenings pulling weeds, unclogging pipes, wiping asses, and coaching sports we no longer had time to play ourselves.

Of course, there were weekends. Spring and winter breaks, too. Often these were the times we locked ourselves in our offices and labs to finally get real work done. We lived busy lives. Full lives. Lives that left us contentedly exhausted at the end of a day. The stress led mostly to harmless, elastic deformation, which is to say we typically bent but did not break. Indeed, some plastic deformation did occur. Our waistlines and brows warped inalterably from much sitting and furrowing. Diego got divorced a couple times. Cambridge lost a lot of money in Atlantic City a lot of times. Eugene's son got arrested (for possession of marijuana) (stolen marijuana) (marijuana stolen from his father).

---

[2] The authors here disclose a more-than-casual interest in blackjack.

So we were tested, yes. As are we all. But never were we strained to fracture. Never were our characters compromised. Our passion for work and life did not diminish. We—the authors—were thankful for this. To still be standing, like Roman arches, thanks to engineering and luck.

Later in our careers, curiosity turned to mastery, passion became profession. Within two decades, all five of us obtained tenure. Our attendance at ASME Conferences declined—the perfunctory parading out of research results no longer necessary for job security. We stayed in touch in small ways. We would fund one another's invited lectures at our respective campuses. We would forward distasteful items from the internet. We would leave voice messages for one another, reading from whomever's paper had most recently been published in a booming, self-aggrandizing voice, or at least a British accent.

These things kept us in touch, yes. But that was not enough. We'd known since the first visit to Reno that we'd need a way to get together on an annual basis. We proposed an alternative conference. Early on, while selecting the locale for this event, we determined the group's centroid—the point at which, if a huge and rigid map of the United States were built and each professor were to stand on his home university, the map would balance on the head of a pin. Three of us worked in the California university system; another in Oregon; one not only worked at MIT, but was quite overweight, providing doubly eastward influence. The centroid was found to be Enoch, Utah. Had it been, say, Las Vegas or even Denver, we might have trusted this calculation as fate. But the Enoch centroid was quickly dismissed as mathematical masturbation. We trusted our guts. And every summer from 1986 to 2008 we went to Reno. The reasons for this choice in venue should, we hope, be quite clear by now.

A full report on the findings from these meetings has not been published, nor would such an account be germane to this study. Suffice it to say that Reno is our Mecca. Our annual pilgrimage has affected the scheduling of weddings, family vacations, birthday parties and two funerals.

The agenda each year is the empty set, denoted { } as per convention, with one exception. The sole artifact of our seminal trip to Reno is a photograph, snapped as an afterthought on our way out of town. In it, we stand abreast across Virginia Street, underneath the Reno Arch, denoted here by Π. Writ large across the arch is the city's famous (and unverifiable) claim to fame: "The Biggest Little City in the World." We look like death and, at the same time, 100% alive. In it, one can clearly see Berkeley's still-damp slacks clinging to his thighs, and a vomit stain on the lapel of Old Crow's sport coat. Eugene's eyes are closed, his head tossed back. Who knows why.

Months later, the film was developed by Diego's girlfriend, who inquired as to how it ended up on her camera, and, more importantly, why she hadn't been told about a visit to Reno. Apparently, this discovery solidified her already gelling concerns regarding capital-T Trust, and the relationship was soon nullified. The next year—and every year since—the only required activity at our meetings has been a re-enactment. The authors arrange themselves under the arch in the same positions and strike the same stupid poses. To hold with tradition we present a handful of casino chips to the passerby who snaps our photo. Then we mail a print to the ex-girlfriend—a gesture she appreciates enough to have kept us informed of address changes over the years. The rest of the conference schedule is improvised. Cards, golf, and *Romeo y Julieta* cigars are customary. Old Crow whiskey is strictly forbidden. Reno's contradictory claim has been adopted for our purposes; the gathering is "The Biggest Little Conference in the World."

$$Eq.\ (2) \qquad TBLCW = \{\ \Pi\ \}$$

MOTIVATION

In January 2009, one of the authors (Old Crow) was diagnosed with pancreatic cancer. By February, the condition had been deemed inoperable. Symptoms included abdominal pain, appetite loss, odd-colored stools, tiredness, nausea, vomiting and weakness.[3] He was placed on bed rest in May. His wife took to caring for him at their home 15 miles east of Eugene, OR.

On the morning of June 26, 2009, { Π } convened under cloudy skies. By mid-afternoon, a thunderstorm had darkened downtown Reno. Rain buffeted our hotel windows. The decision to convene the conference at all had been made to honor our friend. Old Crow had insisted via email that { Π } not suffer just because he was suffering. We made attempts at merriment, debauchery, and depravity, but to no avail. We holed up at a bowling alley bar. We talked about our friend a little. We drank. By 4:30 p.m. we were at a hotel buffet. We ingested gummy slabs of prime rib. We constructed and then deconstructed gooey architectures from the nacho bar. We gaped into the caramelizing flames of bananas foster, feeling sick to our stomachs.

The storm passed. We rode the elevator to the pool on the roof. Mothers were thumbing magazines, their children frolicking in dim orange light. We found a table off in the corner and stunk it up with bitterness and cigars.

The next morning we walked over to the arch, only to forgo our annual rite. To take the photo without the full complement of founding members was, in { Π }'s view, entirely fucked up.

One of the authors (Cambridge) completed his doctorate work at MIT. His thesis on finite element analysis is still widely cited, though perhaps less often than his contribution to MIT's storied hacker legacy. As is custom, he never took credit for his hacks; but when pressed he has no alibi for Halloween night 1962, when the campus' Great Dome was cleverly transformed into a jack-o-lantern wearing a mischievous grin. This stunt, coupled with the authors' ancillary interest in heists (see e.g., D. Ocean et al, 1960, 2001; T. Crown 1968, 1999), and monument magic (D. Copperfield, 1983) prompted a re-evaluation of our photograph, as well as ourselves. That is to say, we stood staring at our reflections in the gilded girders of the arch, facing new and alarming questions—questions that became the genesis of this study: What *real* good had been done over the course of our respective careers? Beyond incremental technological and philosophical advancements within a few engineering niches, what had we to show for ourselves? Who had we truly helped, beyond the call of professional obligation? To whom had we brought joy? We could think of no one.

---

[3] Coincidentally, this is a subset of the symptoms commonly reported by TBLCW attendees.

And yet, we considered ourselves men of means. Sure, we lacked the bravado of youth. But we were salty. We knew things. We kept in decent shape. We played racquetball, ate salmon. We made enough money to buy new European cars every five years. We wore Mephistos. We gripped the purse strings—but also the occasional wrench. There was great leverage in us. Mechanical advantage. All we lacked: purpose. All we needed: someone who needed us.

Over decades of testing, the city of Reno has been shown to possess rejuvenating powers for the authors. The hypothesis tested here is that a surrogate for this holy land can be equally restorative. We posit that the Reno Arch is such a surrogate. Described herein is our attempt at stealing this hallowed structure and moving it. In this case, to our buddy's place near Eugene, Oregon.

MATERIALS & METHODS

There have been many Reno arches over the years, and we expect there will be more in the years to come. The arch in our first photograph was the fifth one. It featured RENO spelled out on four glowing plastic octagons and was topped off with a spiky star. The star rotated. Its look complemented the "mod" signage by then no longer in vogue along Virginia Street. Our next photo, from 1986, featured the current (sixth) arch, the design of which incorporates hints of its predecessors, including the spiky star. It is also the biggest, gaudiest version yet, with more than 2,000 light bulbs, spanning Reno's busiest street, in the brightest part of town, flanked by casinos that never close. On Christmas morning, the casinos are open. On September 12, 2001, they were open. After five minutes of reconnaissance, we concluded that stealing this arch would require a Sikorsky heavy-lift helicopter, liberal volumes of smokescreen, an oxy-fuel cutting torch, and access to the city's electrical controls, among other unobtainables.

In contrast, we came to believe that the fourth Reno Arch—the one spanning Virginia Street from 1934 to 1963 and currently erected as an historical landmark a few blocks away, on quiet Lake Street—was begging for it.

Examine the thing. See its unadorned steel skeleton. Marvel at the rudimentary electrical housing at the base of its western tower. This arch makes a statement. The statement buzzes in all-caps neon: STEAL ME.

The authors took a stroll down Lake Street on a Friday afternoon in June 2009 to case the old arch. Its supporting towers were framed out of slim steel bars, bolted together in a hollow arrangement that made the structure resemble a scale-model steel bridge. The towers were nearly three stories tall. The arch was attached midway up the towers and its apex was slightly lower than the tower tops. Signs bearing the city's name and motto faced both directions of traffic. The joints at the base of each tower were welded; all remaining connections were made with standard nuts and bolts. We jaywalked from sidewalk to sidewalk, pacing off the span: 65 feet, give or take.

We returned Sunday night at 2:00 a.m. and parked just down the street from the arch. We wore matching khakis, work boots, dark green polo shirts, hard hats and walkie-talkies on belt holsters. The street was nearly deserted. We were heavily caffeinated. At 2:17 am, a police cruiser trolled by. As soon as it was gone, three of us jumped out of a rented SUV and set to work.

A 9500-lb reversible wench was secured to the base of the east tower. The nimblest of the authors (Irvine) then scurried up the framework with the wire cable attached to his waist and spooling freely from the winch as he ascended. When Irvine was halfway up the tower, the cable snagged on a rivet, jolting him enough to sever two of the belt loops on his khakis. His hands started to shake. We told him to take a few deep breaths and he swore at us. When he had collected himself, he descended to fix the snag, then started climbing again. Once at the top, he strung the cable through a 9,000-lb pulley he fastened to the underside of the tower, then crawled on hands and knees out to the middle of the arch, where he strung it through another pulley. We needed him to move quicker, but didn't dare distract him. We cringed as he scooted along, two stories above our heads. When a car came he would press his body to the girders and wait for it to pass by below. At last he anchored the cable with a clevis hook to the top of the opposite tower.

The winch was powered up and the gears began to grind. Though we'd tested the winch beforehand, the ratcheting sound it made seemed especially loud on such a quiet street. A dog down by the river started to bark, then another. We looked around, waiting for something to happen. The cable tensed, forming an obtuse 'V' above the arch. Irvine then employed a power drill to remove 34 separate bolts, one by one. Within 20 minutes the arch had been separated from the supporting towers and was hanging between them by a wire, so to speak, although to the casual observer the structure was unchanged.

At this point we radioed Berkeley, who was idling two blocks away in 53-foot flatbed semi we'd rented the day before in Stockton, California.[4] He drove up to the arch from the south and, passing below it, slowed nearly to a stop just as a rowdy group of drinkers surprised us. He drove away. We paused and smiled and did our best to look official. One of the drunks, an attractive young woman, asked what was up. We explained that the arch was being retrofitted to handle earthquakes. She laughed. She was unable to stand without assistance. Someone joked that she could use some retrofitting. She laughed, retched. Meanwhile another car sped by. We waited it out.

When the street was again clear of cars and drunks, we radioed the truck. A minute later it was straddling the road's center line with the middle of the flatbed directly under the arch, perpendicular to it. The wench engaged. The arch descended, leaving the towers standing as shown in Figure 1. Two of the authors tugged on lines tied to the newly free ends of the arch in order to rotate the dangling portion by 90° and set it down lengthwise on the flatbed. Because we'd taken less than the full 65-foot span, the arch hung off the back of the trailer by only two feet. A taxi pulled up behind the trailer. An author standing closest held up his palm and smiled at the driver, who rolled down his window. The author apologized for the inconvenience.

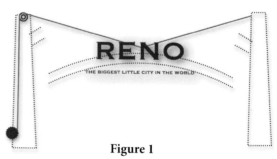

Figure 1

---

[4] Berkeley's sister owned a winery in Sonoma. Since college, he had helped haul cases of wine to customers up and down the state during a few weekends each year. His Class A license was valid.

The driver saluted and lit a cigarette.

Minutes later we reconvened in a dirt lot by the river and finished lashing down the arch. We piled cardboard boxes on it in a few places to mask the trademark curvature and covered the whole thing in a giant canvas tarp.

Irvine started to laugh. It was a tentative laugh, akin to a hissing release valve, and we realized just how nervous he'd been—how nervous we'd all been. What the hell were we doing in this dirt lot in the middle of the night, risking jail time and our jobs for a some ill-conceived prank? What were we trying to prove?

Well: our capacity to create good in the world, for one. But more than likely, this was all just a game of chicken, where none of us wanted to be the one to back down, to call off the fun. And at this point, debate was moot. It was too late to re-hang the arch. We looked around at each other.

Irvine made an observation. He said it looked like we'd kidnapped a dinosaur.

RESULTS

We fled north by northwest to Eugene, Oregon. Two of us in the semi, two in the SUV. We drove through the night and could see little of the country we crossed. The homely florescence of off-ramp gas stations tugged at us—offering cups of coffee, slices of pie, urinals. We didn't even slow down.

Eugene and his wife had retired to a sizable homestead bordering the Willamette National Forest. Daylight found us on worn, two-lane highways that led through cool forests. Pink and yellow wildflowers speckled the ditches, the embankments. More than once, the semi's oversized side mirrors struck overhanging branches. An occasional gap in the trees provided a glimpse of mountains. Blankets of cirrocumulus muted the daylight. We yawned and stretched and felt pretty happy with ourselves.

The drive had passed uneventfully, though we'd clinched our teeth and anuses at every highway patrol cruiser, every dopplering siren. Was there an APB out for the Archasaurus?[5] Or perhaps city officials had been too embarrassed to act at first, waiting for business hours to make calls, assuming the best: something authorized but insufficiently documented was afoot. Retrofit rumors, et cetera.

Despite our somber destination, spirits were high. We shared stories in the cabins of our respective vehicles about noteworthy vacations and exorbitant veterinarian bills, desert golf courses and impending colonoscopies. We talked about Old Crow. A few times we mistakenly, innocently, referred to him in the past tense. We saw our own fates in him. He had been more alive than most anyone we'd known. And suddenly, less. It had come to this so fast. We felt vulnerable, though this feeling went unvoiced. It felt good, though, to be affecting the situation. To be proactive. We were by this point running on hubris and testosterone. Though we hadn't known each other in high school, we believe this is what it would have felt like.

---

[5] That's what we'd taken to calling her by the time we got to Susanville.

None of us had been to the house before. In fact we passed his nondescript mailbox without realizing it until we passed a better-marked box down the road bearing the subsequent address. Knowing we were at least close to the house, we drove another half mile and pulled off the highway onto a gravel road that led uphill through the pines. A few miles in we came to an abandoned barn, behind which we parked the semi. It was 11:48 a.m. We got out to stretch and collect ourselves, yawning in the sunshine. Birds shrieked and whistled from the forest. Any other day, we might have been tempted to nap. But we didn't. We all piled into the SUV and drove back from whence we'd come. We visited various retailers in Eugene in search of a particular item and, having secured it, ate lunch twice, the first meal having failed to get us adequately stuffed and drunk.

Five hours later we were back at the barn. Afternoon shadows crept across the field. A pair of squirrels scurried out from under the big tarp as we pulled up. We sat on the tailgate and opened a bottle of Old Crow and passed it around, cursing cancer through gritted teeth and steeling ourselves.

At 6:45 pm we headed to the homestead. We were clinically intoxicated. Pulling off the road onto the drive, we plunged through a thicket. Here we slowed to a halt amid sighing airbrakes. Crickets throbbed. A diffuse purple darkness hung in the trees. The leaves hung utterly still.

We parked the semi in the weeds beside the drive and all climbed into the SUV. Driving on, we made a few switchbacks over a rise and emerged onto a plateau where the driveway circled a field of mowed grass in front of the house. The house was a nouveau ranch-style place with red metal window frames, granite accents and a wraparound paver porch. Flowers spilled from copper pots tethered to oversized wood beams. To the west there were a pair of outbuildings and a pond dotted with ducks.

A garage door yawned open. A woman ducked under when it was midway up and came out to stand in the gravel. She had a bandana tied about her neck and a pair of leather gloves folded in her hands. We had met our friend's wife years before and this looked much like her, except the hair was whiter, the buttocks droopier. We waved and climbed out to greet her. She squinted at us, reaching into the pocket of her overalls for a pair of glasses. One of us said her name. She nodded, then asked what we were doing on her property. We started to explain. A 16-ounce bottle of Yoo-hoo containing at least 15 ounces of urine tumbled from the SUV and cracked against the running board.

We were not invited inside the house. This was a wall of a woman. We'd come some 470 miles through three states, and our first roadblock was a five-foot, four-inch nag. She berated us. She nodded with disgust at us. She pointed suggestively back to the road. We held up our palms. She shook her head. Her husband was extremely frail, she explained. He drifted in and out of consciousness.

We were skeptical. We'd seen his emails. He'd seemed okay in his emails. We told her as much.

She scoffed. He'd barely had the energy to hold his fork at dinner that evening, she said. And his wishes were simple—peace, solitude, dignity. She was damn well going to grant him these things. Visitors were discouraged, particularly uninvited fugitives. She called our arrival an "ambush."

A fair enough characterization, we agreed. But we knew our motives to be honorable. Unassailable. We were grown men, and we had come to help one of our own. How? she asked. Well, we said, wasn't this all pretty funny? Wouldn't it be a real kick in the prostate for our old pal?

You're drunk, she said. All four of you. She pulled a cell phone from the breast of her overalls and started to dial.

No, no, no, we said. And it went on like this for some time. She stood with poise throughout this debate. A few times she held a handkerchief dramatically over her mouth and nose, perhaps to mask the smell of spilled urine, or just the smell of us. Eventually, we could observe some wear on her psyche. We were getting to her. Our operating assumption was that, deep down, she was a wild one. After all, she *had* married Old Crow, which at least implied a laissez-faire stance on marijuana and the work of J. Garcia et al. Did she also love the second amendment, like our friend? Was she slipping the safety off a pocketed 9mm even as we spoke?

One thing we knew for sure: she loved her husband, probably more than we did. She wanted him happy. So did we. By the transitive property:

$$\textit{Eq. (3)} \qquad \textit{What The Wife Wanted = What The Authors Wanted}$$

It just took a lot of posturing and arguing to derive this equation, is all. And so, some 35 minutes later, we were invited in. At which point we disclosed to her that we had a somewhat sizable gift we'd like to fetch first. Our unwillingness to further disclose the specifics of this gift led to 10 additional minutes of haggling. Reluctantly, she consented to wheel Old Crow into the front room of the house, where he'd be afforded a view of the yard, while we retreated back down the drive in our SUV.

Back at the semi, we performed various and gratuitous impressions of The Wife. We stumbled around, urinating in the bushes like nervy dogs, then set to freeing Archasaurus.

At this point, Diego yanked the starter cord on a generator. Nothing. He yanked again, and again. Nothing, and nothing. We looked around at each other. It was suggested that the carburetor could be gummed up. Old spark plugs were also blamed. Meanwhile the one who'd rented the thing (Diego) kept furiously tugging. Using his legs and hips. With each try came a promising whir, then the sad little zip of retracting cord. Eventually the question on all our minds was broached. Of course he took offense, but we insisted. He unscrewed the fuel cap. Bone dry.

Two gallons of diesel and two inspired yanks later, the generator coughed gray smoke and, after some fumbling with the choke, rumbled to a steady din. The forest flickered and then lit up, bathed in the brilliance of an electrified noble gas. Yellow and white neon penetrated deep into the trees. It was bright as day. Three of us climbed atop the flatbed and sat dangling our feet like kids on a hayride, while Berkeley jogged up to the cab. With a high-horsepower lurch, we were off.

We drove up to the yard, rounded the gravel turnaround and parked outside the picture window. Through the glass we could see Old Crow slumped in a wheelchair, his beloved wife standing beside him. Before she could take aim and shoot us, we hopped down and took up our customary positions under the fully lit arch, leaving an obvious vacancy where Old Crow was supposed to be. The whole side of the house was awash in light. Insects were already congregating. The generator hummed. The big letters of RENO reflected in the window. Through the reflection, Old Crow was smiling ever so slightly, his eyes bright with wonderment. His wife put her hand on his shoulder and his hand crept out from under a blanket and gripped it. This moment is now referred to as the Biggest Little Moment.

We entered the house as heroes. Tea was served. We will not comment on our friend's condition except to say he was sick and extremely tired. During a short chat, he asked many questions about the arch. Throughout the recounting of events he laughed and coughed, laughed and coughed. We didn't wish to overstay our welcome. The Wife was giving us the eye. We were grateful she had humored us. We shook his hand and looked him in the eye. He told us the cancer had stripped away all of the bullshit and exposed him for what he was, which was a weak old fool. It wasn't true, but it made us sad to hear him say it. His hand felt cold when we shook it. Then on our way out he said he wished he could go get arrested with us.

CONCLUSION

The primary question asked in this study was, can a stolen span of steel be of some comfort to a man facing his death? Our answer: sure it can. No further research is necessary. Note: the effect is fleeting. But even arches are fleeting. What's important is that men continue to find good reasons to build arches, to cherish them, and, when necessary, to steal them.

The singular work of D.B. Cooper is worth citing at this point. In 1971, Cooper hijacked a 727 passenger plane, collected $200,000 in ransom money, demanded a fuel stop at the Reno airport and then, once airborne again, strapped the money to his chest and leapt from the plane's rear stairway hatch somewhere over the Pacific Northwest, never to be seen or heard from again. The authors can't help but admire Cooper's panache, and further attest to the innumerable hiding places in the Pacific Northwest. Places where a dinosaur can be released unharmed into the wild. For anyone to find.

Further research is encouraged.

Ben Rogers is just happy to be here. Thanks for having him. He can also be found at readrogers.com.

THE DINNER WAS BLAND

LEAH RUNYON

The dog loved it:
Ribs,
Meet bones
You'll marry
The tightest dress you own.
Outside your house,
there are children wearing crowns,
kings of a suburban square.
Clinging on the sidewalk,
As if they'd lose themselves to
tomorrow.
Emerging from shrubs,
armed with sticks,
Infested with ticks
The things you did and can't admit.

Pucker up,
a spearmint kiss.
Show me your pipe
and we'll blow
bubbles.
Remember how
we chased the glossy sphere
Before it dispersed?
His hands,
an oven
radiating
over your shiny face.
And you,
an indulgence
that ever your dear mother
cannot taste

Leah Runyon is a nineteen-year-old girl born in the quiet suburban sprawl of South Brunswick, New Jersey. She is attending Rutgers University. This is her first major journal publication, and she is excited to see where her writing will take her. As far as extracurriculars, she enjoys taking photos of everything, drinking coffee, and playing the piano.

DRIVE-IN WOMEN

ASHLEY FARMER

IT RAINED AGAINST A MATINEE about danger. M. and I were Friday with no work and there was above us some great beauty driving beautifully across the screen. We hadn't rented the speaker so we couldn't hear her over her fake convertible car moves and all those flat black trees rippling on canvas behind her. Our egos on fire. Everywhere we'd driven that year people asked what kind of women we were becoming. It was dangerous to know, dangerous to not know, and M. dabbed lipstick. Were we even minor beauties? Hardly. The woman's convertible rocked and the woman laughed her teeth because danger was still a distance she hadn't crossed and her face was covered in rainwater. M. had lost the title of her car in the rain. I had lost a map, I had lost an afternoon. I had lost my danger. The bottom corner of the screen ripped, pulled down by an unseen hand, and the woman parked at the edge of black trees and started running. I wanted M. to drive me home in the rain. We couldn't understand the beauty's words, we couldn't remember a time when women drove convertibles without losing their smiles, when they couldn't get too far away in their fake cars, the trees from home so close they could always touch them. M. slid the bottle across the seat. The seats were leather. M. sunk and the sun settled. What kind of women were we becoming? M.'s car was just another car in the rain, not even hers, and water had found its way in. M., I said, drive me home. The wet leather smelled alive. I didn't want to know the ending. This wasn't the kind of woman I was becoming.

Ashley Farmer's work has recently appeared in *Gigantic*, *The Collagist*, *Mud Luscious*, *Fractured West*, and elsewhere in print and online. She lives in Long Beach, California, with the writer Ryan Ridge.

APPALOOSA

RACHEL ADAMS

The heater is broken in my apartment again. I shiver awake from dreams of lying wet in the sand. There are tiny icicles in my bedside glass of water.

I look for a sweater, digging through piles and piles of clothing and not finding, not finding, and it's a Thursday. The phone rings. It's Kathy Richter. I stare at it and mentally tell her what not to say. If she says "Jess, I need your help," I swear, I'll hang up. I have helped Kathy Richter for the last time.

"Jess, you'll never believe," is what she actually says, and this is also bad because I will believe and I am not interested. I make a noncommittal noise.

"Evelyn died."

I am silent. She is listening maybe for me to start crying, and when I don't she says, "No surprise, I guess. Bitch was always flaking on us."

I find myself falling back in love with her.

"Come over and we'll have 'our best friend died' sex," she says.

I picture the way her lips stick together between words in that bright pink lipstick she has worn since the sixth grade. Maybe it's a trap. Maybe I'll get there ready for a little what-have-you and find myself instead heading to Costco for her favorite brand of cough drops. Again.

"Have you called the others?"

"Yes," she says. "They're coming over tonight. So hurry."

Her building is a ramshackle box. The black paint on the railings comes off on my hands and I stare at the pattern, which looks like a dog humping another dog. This probably means I'm a sexual deviant.

As I knew she would (why wouldn't she), Kathy opens the door wearing nothing but high heels. "I'm such an unholy mess of a girl," she says.

"Hello, Red."

She lowers her eyelashes. "Come in."

Her bush is bright red to match her hair, which is new. I comment on it.

"You're not supposed to use the box dye for pubes. It tingled for days." She pulls out a chair for me and I sit, staring at her paleness as she lounges against the counter.

I'm tingling myself.

Until I see the coffin.

Hairs all over me stand up. "What's that?"

She raises an eyebrow. "Don't you mean who?"

I give her a long look. She smirks, so I walk across the room. I raise the lid and look inside. I close it and turn to face Kathy Richter. "What's she doing here?"

"You really need to calm down." She crosses the room and sits on the floor in front of the couch, lights her pipe, inhales deeply, and regards me with criticism. Even as she coughs, the criticism is there.

"I am calm," I say.

"You're breathing through your nostrils."

I wonder if the carpet where she's sitting will smell of her.

"Do you want some?" she asks. I shake my head and sit beside her. "So," she leans into my face, and I think she's going to blow smoke at me but she puckers her lips off to the side to exhale. She reaches over and grabs my bulge with a rough upward motion that makes me wince. "What now?"

There are goose bumps on her tits. My nose grazes hers as I turn my head to look at the coffin again. "Why is she here?"

Kathy releases me. She shrugs. "Where else would we hold the viewing?"

"I thought she secretly hated you?"

"Yes, that's right, she hated me." The bowl is finished. She bends over scowling, pinching and crushing buds from a crumpled baggie with one elbow in the air. "Look, Jess, it's now or never, okay? They'll be here at half past."

I sigh and take off my pants, struggling to pull them over my shoes, because Kathy Richter hates it when I do that, when my dick hangs out just below my shirt and my socks are limp around my ankles, says it makes me look like a little boy. She doesn't notice, but I can't stand there waiting for her to be annoyed, so I pull off my shoes and yank off my shirt and hoodie all tangled up together, because she hates that too.

I suddenly feel tender love for our past arguments. She catches me looking her in the face and hands me the pipe, watches me with big redshot eyes as I light up.

I lean down. Smoke drifts from her nostrils as I kiss her, and for some reason this reminds me of the Appaloosa my grandfather owned when I was young, a mare who would sit quiet and quiver while I talked to her, my face against the velvet of her nose. I was ten and watched a lot of cowboy shows, had ideas about what a man and a beast could be. The summer ended, the horse died. In my memories she follows me across the field, nudges me with her great head, but I also remember pockets full of carrots.

As though sensing my shift in mood, Kathy Richter stands abruptly and leads me, business-like, into the bedroom. The winter light touches her skin blue and stony and it's enchanting when I find her warm and soft underneath me.

■

Three minutes later I'm apologizing from the bedroom as Kathy Richter digs through kitchen drawers for cigarettes. Outside the winter trees extend like arteries into the sky. The front door opens loudly. Josh Gates' loud "Hi!" turns into embarrassed laughter and protest as Kathy shoos him out again. She comes back into the bedroom and digs in the closet for a baggy sweater and skinny jeans and pulls them over her naked body, slipping her feet out of, then back into the three-inch black heels, which she hasn't taken off this entire time. "Ouch," she says.

"What?"

"Zipper's cold."

I lean over to breathe it warm and she gives me a look.

"What?"

"You're trying too hard."

I sit alone in the room and try not to feel sorry for myself.

"Why the fuck are you so early?" I hear her say to Josh.

"I thought I was late."

"Five thirty, dickweed, not five."

Josh laughs again. "So I'll leave?"

"Come in."

Once when I was giving Kathy a back massage, she told me that they had made love once. She and Josh. "He cried," she said, and looked really happy about it. Now every time I see him I picture him naked, crying into her red hair because of the sex.

I pull on my pants and stand in the doorway. Josh sees me and grins a dopey grin.

"I think I'm out of coffee filters," says Kathy Richter. My heart plummets but right away she says "Never mind, here they are."

Josh goes through her records and pulls out Supertramp. Kathy hears the opening chords of "Goodbye Stranger" and frowns at him.

"Really, Josh?"

Josh shrugs. I shrug too and bob my head to the music. Kathy walks over to change it. Josh puts a hand on her arm. "Evelyn wanted it."

"She hated prog rock." Kathy Richter won't let us see the album she's exchanging it for. She sits beside us on the mint green faux-leather sofa. We stare at the coffin.

"Bjork?"

"There's no accounting for taste," she says. We continue to stare at the coffin. Kathy is wearing yellow rubber dishwashing gloves. She always puts them on to make coffee; I've never gotten a good explanation out of her.

"Why do you even have this album?" asks Josh. Under his good humor I can tell he is annoyed.

"Bjork?" Steve pokes his head in the door.

"Does anyone knock anymore?"

"I thought it was an open house." Annette is with him. She has a new bob that makes her look like a flapper with her elegant, lazy limbs. I've always wanted to fuck Annette and I think she wants it too but one of us has always been dating someone else. She sits down in the exact spot where Kathy was sitting earlier and she's wearing a short skirt. I'm slightly aroused for most of the wake.

The pipe is lit again, passed around. Steve produces a bottle of gin of which everyone takes a sip. I feel the need for a speech.

"Well," I say. "We are all here together—"

"Oh lord," says Kathy.

"Let him speak." Annette is rewarded with a bored look. I clear my throat.

"Life. What is life? There is no meaning. This is all an illusion anyway. Empty spaces. There is no meaning."

I pause and everyone nods solemnly. Kathy Richter is sitting cross-legged. I remember she's wearing those jeans commando. It takes me a moment to get back on track.

"Which, if you think about it, is pretty fucking amazing. And wonderful. Way to participate in this experience, Evelyn. Whether it means nothing. Whether you are now enlightened as to what this shitfuck was all about. You did it, you're done. Good job."

They clap. Kathy sighs. God, she looks good.

"Anyone else?" she asks.

Josh grins vacantly and Annette shrugs. "I brought a casserole," she says.

"We need a hearse," says Kathy Richter. "Jesse? Your seats fold down, don't they?"

We all heft the coffin. With exorbitant cursing, sweating, and maneuvering, we manage to get it—her—Evelyn—out the door, down the stairs, and into my gold station wagon. Somewhere in the course of all of this the mood has changed. We are quiet and solemn.

Kathy stands by the passenger door. "Steve? Your move."

"I've got a place in mind," he says. He looks uncomfortable. "It's nothing like what she wanted, but it's too cold to dig—"

"Great," says Kathy. "Jesse and I will follow you, and Josh can follow us."

■

It's dark as Kathy's bush pre-dye by now. The moon turns everything to silver shadows. Our caravan rolls on through the canyon, Evelyn's coffin playing corners in my backseat, sometimes sliding into our headrests when we go down a steep hill. I rest a hand on Kathy Richter's knee. The muscles twitch slightly but her face registers nothing. Steve makes a turn and I follow him though I can't see the dirt road until I'm on it. Now it's bumpy and rocks of various sizes are hitting my undercarriage and I grip her thigh. This goes on for twenty-odd minutes— bump, rocks, thigh—and then Steve pulls over. We're right up against the mountain. I give her thigh a pat as we get out.

"It's fucking cold," says Annette, holding onto her elbows. She hasn't got a coat, only a cardigan, and she's wearing strappy sandals. She blows into her hands. "Just like her to die in January."

Josh winces. His face is pale and I can't tell in the dark but I think he's been crying. This is his third funeral in a year—his grandma and baby cousin were killed in a car accident when grandma fell asleep at the wheel. I hug him awkwardly. He gives me a funny look.

"This way," calls Steve, blinding us all in a row with his flashlight. "It's not far."

The snow is deep but it's too cold to melt—lucky, or we'd all be soaked. None of us is prepared for a hike in the woods though Evelyn told us again and again it's where she wanted to be. Me, I just want to be burned crispy. Nothing to rot and degenerate further.

Steve stops and turns to us as we each catch up. We form an uneven half circle around him. He points.

"A cave?" I say. "You want to shove her in a cave?"

"It's really shallow, Steve," Josh says. "Won't someone find her?"

Steve points the light at the floor of the cave. Near the back is a chasm. We venture inside, peer into the depths. Though it's hard to see from the mouth of the cave, it's wide enough that I could probably drive my station wagon into it. The weak flashlight beam reveals nothing but jagged walls. Kathy Richter leans over, picks up a pebble, and drops it into the darkness. We listen. There is no sound—at least none that we can hear past the chattering of Annette's teeth.

A shiver passes over me.

"Okay," she says. "Let's go get her."

■

We stand outside the cave, looking from the coffin to the hole. "Now what?" says Steve.

"We need rope."

Kathy Richter looks at me. Everyone else looks at me. As I walk to the car I remember the look on her face when I came, her eyes blinking, her lips set. I turn around.

"Why don't we just shove it in?"

"What if it busts open on the way down?" Annette asks.

I shrug.

There is silence. Josh wants to say something. He doesn't.

Kathy's heels leave little sunken squares on the frozen earth as she walks to the casket. She kneels in the cold dirt and gives it an experimental push. Heavy as it is, it moves a bit, grating against the cave floor with a noise like a cluster of angry bats.

"Let's do it."

All five of us get behind the coffin and push together. It slides almost of its own volition and tips before we're ready. Josh and I land on our faces. We hear the coffin tumble and scrape its way down the rough walls—then nothing.

I grab the flashlight and point it into the darkness. The coffin is wedged at an odd angle between the walls of the chasm about ten feet down. "Ah shit," I say.

Annette puts her hand on my back to steady herself as she takes a look. Kathy Richter and I exchange glances and then, right at the same moment, begin to snicker. Josh sits in the dirt with his back against the cave wall and his hands covering his face. I get the feeling he is not laughing.

Steve pulls Annette back from the edge and folds her into his arms. She is babbling. "We can't leave her like that. It's dark and cold. She's only halfway there. We have to do something."

"This is bad," he says. He pushes his glasses up his nose. "What we did is illegal. They're going to find her and people will be upset."

"They who? What people?" says Kathy Richter. "Her parents don't care." Her laughter is high-pitched now, something like a whinny. This thought makes me laugh even harder. Tears start to roll down my fuck-up cheeks. I scoot back from the edge and lean against Kathy, and she leans against me.

"Good idea," Josh says. He is definitely crying. "Good fucking idea, guys."

We become sober. Annette is still shaking, Steve frowning at the chasm as he lights a cigarette. Kathy inserts herself into the crook of my arm and pulls my hand into her pocket.

"Stroke my hair?"

I place my hand, stiff with cold, on Kathy Richter's red mane and pet it and pet it. I whisper, "That a girl. That a girl."

Rachel Adams was raised better than to write about sex, death, and animals. She's an assistant editor for the *Black Warrior Review* and an MFA in fiction at the University of Alabama. Sometimes she says things at selfprophecy.blogspot.com.

AFTERSCHOOL FIRES

LINCOLN MICHEL

There is nothing I love more than an autumn fire
at the wood's edge. An old log is rolled over
for a bench and sparks leap through the air

like angry red spiders. Boys hiding beneath their
baseball hats forage in the woods for sticks. Another
carefully lifts out a soda can that has been pressed

into the embers until it reaches a neon glow. It is almost
liquid. Droplets hiss into the fire. The boy carries
the glowing can behind an old oak tree. He is just beyond

the fire's sight and, dropping his pants, unleashes his
stream. It sounds like a miniature war, all hiss and crackle
and oh my god, the smell! (You thought burning hair

was bad.) Smoke surrounds him as the others scream
or yell or laugh. Seeing the look on his face you might
take him for a rotten, troubled boy. And he is that.

His grades are poor and his mother beats him with
a curling iron. But this is not why he pisses with such force.
He is pissing not just against the coming winter—although

it will be cold—but against that dim expanding cave
we call the future. How much longer can this last?
In a few years the soda will be replaced with beer.

Then it is off to school in the city (community college
most likely) and there are no fires there. His friends will go
their separate ways. The girls will be cold and the work

hours long and boring. His belly will grow round above his jeans. But now it is fall and someone has just tossed an entire bag of marshmallows into the flames.

So piss, I say! Let forth every drop until nothing is left but wet aluminum ash and the cloud of piss-smoke drifts slowly away into the dark, dark woods.

THE LAST OF OUR GRANDFATHERS

LINCOLN MICHEL

The old man caught the champagne cork and plugged it right into the middle of his chest. We'd found him in a breadbox behind the bus station. He was rolled in powders and chewing on his own leg. "There will be no more celebrations for a thousand years," he said. How could we have known he had prophecy in his heart? The devil! His palms were stamped in gold leaf and storm clouds dragged him back and forth across town like strings in a school play. No one received anything in the mail that wasn't a bill. Kissing each other in the dark of the library, we found an ancient book that told of a magic sword. I had to ride on the last of our smuggled balloons to fetch it from the golden eagle's nest. We found the old man in the park stitching shut the beaks of songbirds. After the blade pierced his wheezing heart, the storm clouds mourned for a hundred days. This is how the great lakes were formed.

Lincoln Michel's work appears in *The Believer*, *NOON*, *The Oxford American*, *elimae*, and elsewhere. He is a co-editor of *Gigantic* and the Books Editor of *The Faster Times*. He keeps an infrequently updated personal blog at lincolnmichel.com.

I DREAM OF CARL

LANIA KNIGHT

I arrive, alone, in Vermont in the middle of March. The painters and writers and sculptors who got here two weeks earlier already know each other. I don't know anyone, but before me stretches two weeks of no cooking, no folding laundry, no helping anyone with homework. All I have to do is write. My husband and teenage sons are home in Missouri, and finally, I have time to myself. After the welcome tour and quiet unpacking of my suitcase, I go to my studio. The heavy door closes behind me, and I turn the deadbolt. I arrange my books and pictures and lists on the shelves. Just out the window unfolds a view of the snowy banks of the frozen Gihon River. I sit at the desk and open my new, empty notebook. And I am already lonely.

Carl is one of the painters. He and I pass each other several times that first day walking in opposite directions across the bridge spanning the Gihon River. He is bright and sunny. Twenty-five, tall and broad-shouldered with impish blue eyes. Soon he is calling to me each time he sees me—drawing out the first syllable of my name and then the second so it sounds like something fun, exciting, not just a word for a middle-aged female writer shuttling over the icy, churning water to her writing studio.

Midweek, on a sunny afternoon, I stand on the bridge where my phone can get a signal. I call Karla, a dream therapist I've been working with for two months. One mitten is hugged under my arm so the fingers of my free hand can press the right buttons. My nose runs, I wipe it, and I begin pacing to shake off the cold. I don't call her from my studio, where it is warm, out of respect for the other writers working quietly on their manuscripts.

Karla lives in Vermont, only an hour south of the artist colony. I email her my dreams every other week, and she consults with her teacher at North of Eden, a center for archetypal dreamwork in northern Vermont. Then, twice a month, Karla and I have a session, like this one, where we discuss the archetypal patterns in my dreams and what they are showing me about my life. I am giddy to hear her voice, to tell her how my writing is going.

"How is your homework going?" she asks, meaning the work she gave me the last time we talked, the dipping back into my dreams to re-experience feelings and images.

"I've been distracted," I tell her. Traveling has kept me from thinking about my last dream, the one where a snake bit me on both of my hands.

"Remember," she says, "the snake venom is an antidote, not a poison. It awakens you to what you need to see next." What I saw next in that dream was a woman trapped on a hospital bed, her head in a metal clamp.

"It's okay," Karla says, "If you are struggling with your homework."

I'm pacing on the edge of the bridge, careful of the cars swerving to miss the potholes in the crumbling asphalt. "I'm sorry," I tell her.

She reassures me, her voice tender and quiet. "Being aware that you are far away from your homework is a big step," she tells me. She asks if I'm ready to talk about my most recent dream.

"Yes," I say, distracted by a twinge of shame at not doing my homework.

I continue pacing, wiping my nose again. Karla asks me if I can sit on a bench and close my eyes. I do, and I try to see the cave in my last dream, the friend who is descending to the bottom alongside me, a little manta ray hiding near a rock in a pool of water. My shame shifts to curiosity about the creature and about the water, cool on my feet in the dream. There are no artists walking nearby, no writers scurrying to the dorms. I close my eyes and hear the water rushing beneath the ice that encrusts the Gihon River. I sink into the dream, the cave, the little manta ray.

Karla gives me new homework: to step into the water and notice how it cools me after the heat of the cave and to feel my attraction to this small water animal. The friend in the dream is the feminine form of the divine, according to Karla, and she is walking with me as I find my way deeper into the cave, into the water. In dreams, water represents essence, our deepest self.

For days, I write, eat, sleep, think about my cave dream, and I write some more. Near the end of the second week, I get to dance with Carl. The session is almost over—everyone will be leaving soon—so the younger artists and writers are putting together a dance party. I buy a cheap bottle of white wine that evening at the little supermarket by the post office and bring it to the party. I sip my cupful slowly, waiting for what Margaret, one of the young writers, says is the right time to turn down the lights and turn on the music.

I'm here to dance. In any crowd, I'm the first to start moving, always impatient for the music to start, the lights to dim, the permission to get on the floor. My longing to dance infuriated my first husband. In our twelve years together, I danced only twice. In the first few months after he divorced me, I sprung from our marriage, freed from a trap. I danced, I went to parties, I swam in Ozark streams in Missouri by moonlight. Here in Vermont, though, years later, I feel shy, old, and out of place.

When Carl shows up at the party, he doesn't wait for the lights to be dimmed as Margaret says he should. He doesn't wait for someone to find good dance music. He has his own corny playlist on an iPod and he hooks it into an amp. He dances. Crazy, bent-kneed dancing, like a rooster. I join him. We spin, stomp, slip around until I can hardly hold myself up. His body is so young and strong—he can do anything on the dance floor. I try to keep up, feeling the weight of my own body tugging at me. Dancing with him feels like being carried by a version of my younger self. He isn't attracted to me. I wouldn't mind if he were—that would be flattering. But he doesn't see me that way. It's freeing.

Just before the big exodus when all sixty artists and writers will leave Vermont, Carl visits me in my writing studio. He has shown me his studio, has explained what gouache paint is and let me watch as he worked on a painting of a hippopotamus peeking from behind palm fronds, bits of paper taped to the wall nearby, torn edges and asymmetrical shapes. He has a philosophy of balance: the beautiful and the ugly, funny and sad. When he comes to visit me in my studio, we whisper about life and art so as not to bother the other writers in rooms nearby, musing on the Francis Bacon art book on my shelf left by someone else, talking of plans for our futures. He tells me he'll be traveling my way in the summer, driving from his parents' house in Maryland to an art school in Oregon, and he wants to know—can he stay with me? Of course, I say, never believing he really will.

■

My husband will be out of the country when Carl is passing through, and he is nervous, I think, about having this 25-year-old rock-climbing painter stay with me alone. In May, three months before Carl is due to arrive, I have a dream about him.

It is in three parts. In the first part, I'm sitting at a table in the restaurant of an old hotel under an archway connecting two rooms. A parade of people is going by—they are noisy, but I'm near the wall, watching as the crowd passes. Two police officers with guns and badges are checking everything—the dimensions of the arch, whether the furniture will move around, structural stuff. I hear a deep, low noise from far away and am instantly thrilled. I want to rise to my feet and go to the noise. I know the deep rumble is coming from a huge tiger in a cage. I'm exhilarated and terrified.

In our session for this dream, I call Karla from a parking garage back home in Missouri. I am closed up tight in the solitude of my car. I need privacy from my sons coming home from school, my husband coming back from work.

I rest my notebook on the steering wheel. Karla says that in the archetypal world, all is healed. "If something goes wrong," she says, "it's okay. You're being called to the archetypal world by the tiger – it is calling your soul."

She talks more, and I try to take good notes. The homework she gives me is to follow the tiger's call; when I get into the places where I am feeling responsible for everyone else, go to the place in the dream of belonging, of being filled with excitement and terror.

The next part of the dream is about Carl: I'm up in the cab of a huge truck, sitting on his lap. He leans into me and I have my hand on his leg. We start kissing. At first, I'm thinking about being a good kisser, about technique, but then I realize we've been kissing for a long time. Karla explains that Carl is the animus, the male form of the divine—he is in direct relationship with me in an intimate way. He comes to me in this young alpha male character because I can accept him like this. This is about me, not about my husband or any other lovers. Karla says my intimacy with the animus is about my soul.

I don't really believe in souls or god or the divine, so I take in what she says, write more notes and consider altering some of the words to fit with my view of the world. I want to do deep emotional work because I have stopped taking the antidepressants my doctor prescribed me for seven years, and I don't want to go back. I don't want to get sucked into the recurrent depression that has dogged me for decades. I won't let the language come between me and the work I have to do to stay off of those pills. So I write down what she says.

In the third part of the dream, I'm driving on a highway at night and it's starting to rain. I'm going to a rec center. I walk up to the side door, carrying Daniel, my son, in a car seat—he's a toddler. I'm wet and he's wet and it's dark and I'm trying to get into this building. A guy in a long coat with dark hair in a ponytail walks up. He seems menacing, but he opens the door for me, and then he is walking away. An animal in the shape of a man with a smallish head is following him.

Talking about this part of the dream with Karla irritates me. She keeps asking about this creature, what he looks like, how I feel about him, do I like him. She points out that I called the small creature "inconsequential," and she tells me that actually, this creature is the part of me that will do anything to follow the animus, no matter how ridiculous or needy. It is separate from me because I haven't taken it inside myself. The dream is showing me my need to be with my soul self – the needy, inconsequential creature – in connection with the animus.

At the end of the session, I remember something I haven't thought of in years, decades. It is a beautiful summer day and Jerry, a kid who lived down the street from me briefly when I was in elementary school, is lying next to me on the grass. My cat has just had kittens—they are old enough that she will let us touch them and hold them. This memory is one of few where I am young and feeling the sensuality of it all—the grass, the sunshine, kittens and soft fur, Jerry next to me laughing and caught up in kittens mewing and pawing at his neck—but it isn't sexual.

I knew a lot about sex by the time I was in first grade: a young neighbor blackmailed me into giving and receiving oral sex. When I confessed to my mom, waiting in the car with her while my big brother went through drills on the football field in front of us, she didn't punish me. I hoped she would forgive me, and she did—she told me I never had to do it again. The incident, though, was one of dozens of sexual encounters during my childhood that ultimately warped my understanding of intimacy, sensuality, and sex. The memory with Jerry and the kittens, its lack of sexual undertones, is a rare gem unearthed by the dream work.

In the week following my session with Karla, part of my homework, to hear the call of the tiger from the first part of the dream and the terror and excitement, releases more memories of childhood. My family is from New Orleans, but we moved to Texas when I was two. We traveled back to the city often, especially for Mardi Gras. My grandmother and her sister dressed up and waited all day in folding chairs for beads and doubloons, no matter the weather or the crowds. I lived for catching someone's eye on a passing float, snatching a set of beads from the air thrown directly at me. And I lived for the St. Augustine marching band. Every member was black, with metal helmets and shiny purple and gold uniforms, playing music in unison and marching, yet each one moving differently—saxophones swinging one way, clarinets another, trumpets shot out into the gyrating crowds, snare drums and bass drums and cymbals beating out a rhythm that was unstoppable. That was my experience of terror and excitement—the drumming and music of St. Augustine. So I think about it whenever I can, leading to more memories, like my first husband never letting me dance, calling it a public display of sexual desire. I recognize now that when I left home with him at sixteen, I didn't know I was also leaving behind the thrill of dancing and music.

As I continue my homework, I see that when I am lonely, I project onto men qualities they don't possess, qualities I find attractive. The wake up call comes from a conversation during the summer with a photographer. We are talking about his next book, ideas for how to arrange his photos and his essays. We keep going back and forth—I say something like, what if you chose a handful of photos and then wrote an essay connecting them.

"What do you think?" I ask.

He tries to say it back to me. "You mean, do this?" he asks, and he rambles for a moment.

"No," I say. I try to explain what I mean again. But he doesn't get it.

"Well, maybe you already know what you want to do," I say. "You just need time to let it come forward." And then I realize he is attracted to me and can't hear me because he is projecting something onto me, an image of someone who isn't me. He can't see the real me or hear what I am saying. I'm getting a taste of what it is like for men when I project onto them—I don't see them for who they are, but rather, who I want them to be.

■

When it is time for Carl to arrive at my house in August, I devise a few safeguards—I have my kids come home from their dad's house; I make Carl's bed downstairs, in my studio, far away from my own bed. I've planned for us to go to Six Flags—something fun and intense to match his fun, intense personality, but then one thing after another goes wrong when I get home from my own travels on the road, and I'm not ready to have that much fun. I scale our excursion down to a small swimming hole nearby. But I am exhausted and on my period, bleeding so heavily I don't even feel up to a little swim. We go to my favorite bakery for breakfast, with my sons, and then we go home and Carl and I sit in the creek bed at the edge of my backyard and talk for several hours. I still notice how strong and young his body is—a version of who I'd wanted to be when I was young. There is the possibility of sexual attraction—of knowing myself and how I'm always checking out guys. As a result of my dream work, though, I am aware of my own projections. And again, like at the artists' colony, I know it just isn't there for him. He isn't attracted to me in that way. Instead, there is a different kind of vulnerability that comes with talking, asking questions, telling each other our stories. I feel connected to him.

At one point in the conversation, I mention I never intended to get pregnant. I have two kids. He asks what happened. I go on for too long about my ex-husband and our lack of contraception. Carl is attentive as I speak, and the story is interesting, so it isn't until I'm done that I realize he's asked because he really needs to tell me something. He waits a minute, throws a few stones across the creek bed, and then sighs and smiles into the shade of the branches hanging over us from the trees along the bank. He tells me he is worried he might have gotten a girl pregnant. He *always* wears condoms. Always, except for this one time. No one else knows, besides him and the girl, and now me.

It is a huge burden to carry alone. I've been in situations where I was vulnerable and advantage was taken, like when my neighbor pulled the covers over us and put her head between my legs. Carl is so young, not yet fully formed. Even though he is over six feet tall and could carry me on his back up the side of Half-dome, I have fifteen years of life experience that he does not. He is on my turf. His confession makes him more vulnerable.

I don't take advantage. Instead, I just *see* him, a young man who needs someone to talk to, and I realize how the old way I had of projecting onto men could have been disastrous. He could never have said what he needed to say. He wouldn't have been safe with me.

A new possibility is opening up before me—I touch a rock lying next to me in the dry creek bed, feel the ridges of a crinoid's indentations, then look back at Carl, seeing him not as a sexy twenty-five year-old, but as a vulnerable human being who needs to unload a great burden. I've been doing my dream homework, and I am changing.

Carl leaves my house that afternoon in his packed station wagon, headed west to begin work on his MFA in art. He plans to make stops along the way, maybe in Colorado or at Kleinshmidts near Odessa, Missouri, for cowboy boots. He texts me two weeks later: *not a dad.*

Lania Knight lives in the flatlands of Illinois. Her work has recently appeared or is forthcoming in *New Stories from the Midwest*, *Midwestern Gothic*, *Jabberwock Review*, and others. She misses three-dimensional topography, and still likes to dance.

ATMOSPHERIC DISCHARGES OF ELECTRICITY ACCOMPANIED BY THUNDER

FRANK HINTON

Rain slaps the window glass of an apartment. The apartment is silent but for the rain. A man sits at the kitchen counter, his girlfriend sits on a chair in the living room. It is an open concept apartment. The place is dim and lit only by a muted television. The weather channel is on and it doesn't look good. The man in the kitchen examines a carton of milk. He's really puzzled over the expiry date. A bowl of granola rests on the counter. The girlfriend stares at the muted television. She's draped over the chair. Her leg sways in dilatory spasmodic arcs that play in silent tempo to the rain.

There are a lot of things between them, physically. There's a large wooden table, a hamper full of clothes, candy wrapper empties scattered on the counter, a counter, the floor. There's a little village of boxes all stuffed with goods. Some boxes say FRAGILE because they have glass in them and are fragile. They're like ten feet apart, this guy and girl. All kinds of air is between them and a million or so dust motes glide around without direction. The guy and girl blend with the miscellanea. The lights are off making shadows from shape.

Everything is wet too. It's been raining for two months solid. It's been raining non-stop all over the country, all over the world.

A static weather forecast frames in the television. Rain today, tomorrow and the next. Potential graupel on Saturday. The weather lady isn't even smiling. All kinds of little animated meteorological effects explode and repeat as the weather lady steps from New York to California. Her breasts bounce as she walks.

The girlfriend turns to her boyfriend who's watching the weather lady's breasts bounce as sour milk falls over his granola. The girlfriend can smell the milk from her chair. There are small bacterial clumps falling from the milk carton that the guy doesn't see because they're hidden by the milk stream. The milk isn't even white so much as yellow. In all the tenebrousness it just looks like milk. The boyfriend's name is Michael. It says so right on his housecoat. Full name. *M-i-c-h-a-e-l.* He's fixed on the weather lady, Amanda Wallace. His granola is drowning. Amanda Wallace walks across screen again, bouncing.

Michael's girlfriend makes a half smile and turns back to the television. They had just finished having morning sex and Michael's still able to fantasize. Michael's girlfriend's hand finds the remote and her finger finds the channel button and she finds a station showing some vintage wrestling match. This channel's got more static than the last.

Michael makes a face as he mouths a spoonful of granola. Some milk escapes his mouth and streams down his beard to a drip from the chin. He wipes the dripping with his housecoat sleeve and tosses the spoon into the cereal. He starts to cough and it's like, all phlegmy. Now a bit of mucous is running down over previously dried mucous flakes on his philtrum and upper lip. He pulls some air in and lets it out. He'd sneezed all over the place during morning sex.

"I'd love a milk," he says.

The girlfriend smiles. She's wearing a housecoat too and her name's on it. *Carolyn*. Carolyn turns and eye-to-eyes Michael and spreads her leg a bit in a motion that isn't intentionally suggesting arousal but also isn't prohibiting it. She's wearing a little thong that does not fully cover the pubis. She's thin and etiolated and sexy.

"I'd love to go grocery shopping," she says and her smile widens. "It's funny the more you try to preserve milk, the faster it goes sour, it seems. I thought we timed that one right."

Michael smiles and works his way to the couch. His feet make little splashing sounds as he walks through the puddles on the floor. His rubber boots squeak. All around the windows drool with rain. There is thunder some distance away.

As Michael sits down Carolyn stands up. She closes her robe and puts a finger on Michael's shoulder as she walks by. She smells the sour milk in the kitchen. Carolyn opens the fridge and there's light. The kitchen turns unnaturally pale. The only real food in the fridge is celery. The rest is just crumbs and stale things too precious to throw out. In the cupboard she finds the peanut butter and calculates how many knifefuls of the stuff she has left. She takes a sliver of PB and slides it into the browning gutter of a celery stick.

Michael watches television and a masked wrestler performs a double-underhook suplex on his opponent. The opponent falls to his back and swells red with fake pain and climbs to his feet. The masked wrestler takes a fistful of his opponent's hair and pulls him up onto his feet. It seems time for a finisher. Then someone comes from behind them, a third wrestler holding a steel chair. All of this happens in a storm of static. The chair crashes across the spine. The masked wrestler goes down.

Carolyn wonders when the Milkman will come. Lyle the Milkman is a sort of local hero. He's apparently got dominion over some of the non-raided grocery stores. He spends his days ferrying from apartment to apartment in this neighborhood delivering food, candles and stuff like that. He likes it when you call him Milk-man.

Carolyn takes a bite of her celery. She imagines asking Lyle to flex and feeling his biceps, hard and veined from lifting all those supplies. Carolyn inspects her snack. The ratio of peanut butter to celery is askew. Carolyn's mind enters a complex thought helix involving less watery celery, the Milkman's genitals, and some abstruse intimate act in a warm, dry velvet-filled and candle-lit bedroom.

The masked wrestler is still aching from the chair to the back. It doesn't help that the opponent and his chair wielding abettor are kicking away at the masked man's torso. Michael notes bloodstains on the mat from a previous bout. He watches sweat leak from the two attackers. It, the sweat, drips from their noses, their pecs, their arms, the ends of their long and dyed hair. Sweat drips from beneath the mask of the masked man.

Watching wrestling makes Michael feel strong. Michael bets to himself that Amanda Wallace, the weather lady is turned on by Lucha masks.

Carolyn finishes her celery and goes into the bedroom. The bedroom is carpeted and the carpet is in a state of permanent soak. Everything is soaked. The towels they use to dry themselves before getting into bed are soaked. There are no windows in the bedroom, it's the blackest room in the apartment. It's always cold.

Michael watches as the masked wrestler is defeated by submission. His legs are pretzel in a figure-four and he taps on the blood stained mat. The opponent refuses to let go though, even after the bell rings. The submission continues as the referee is hit with a chair. The nonsense thrills Michael.

"Want to fool around?" Carolyn calls from the bedroom.

"Is there any mouthwash left?"

They strip in the dark and have sex to the sound of motor boat engines whirring around in the flooded streets below. Their feet are wet. Michael does his best to hide his dyspnea. It, the sex, has a kind of Rube-Goldberg quality. It's a kind of jazz routine they perfected in the darkness. The sex is an escape from boredom. They are pretty much soundless. Carolyn doesn't want Michael to sneeze on her, like last time. She doesn't want to wipe herself down with a wet towel. Michael coughs and rubs his nose on his shoulder. Carolyn pretends not to notice and stares off at the wall. Carolyn thinks of Lyle the Milkman. Michael thinks of Amanda the weather lady. When Michael finishes he pins Carolyn to the mattress.

"1..2..3. Ding ding ding."

They are laying in the dark talking about cigarettes and the front door opens. There are people talking. Michael and Carolyn just listen.

"-one bedroom but a really nice skyline. You can see there is minimal flooding compared to the last place we looked at. No carpet except in the bedroom. Open concept kitchen, island, nice wide living room. This district still gets electricity and hot water, though you might see some discoloration...nothing like the two bedroom on Morris Avenue."

It's a realtor and some sweet little couple. Michael gets dressed and wanders down the hallway. The realtor, named Rachel gives a half smile when she sees Michael.

"You're supposed to be down in the common room," she says. Her teeth are so fucking white it's commercial.

"We thought you were showing tomorrow. See. We're packing."

Michael points to the half-stuffed moving boxes on the floor.

"Can we get some light in here?" the man asks. He's old and he's wearing overalls and he's got gold rings clamping the fat on three of his fingers. His wife is even fatter. She's round and rose-eyed and def. thinking about whether that unfinished bowl of granola on the counter is still edible. She's licking lips and squinting in the dim. Miiilk.

Carolyn sits in the room and doesn't move. Last time Rachel the Realtor came over there was a kerfuffle. In the flood, storied apartments were prime. Michael has accepted eviction but Carolyn hasn't. This apartment belonged to her grandmother.

While Rachel leads the old woman into the bedroom Carolyn sits with her legs wide open and uncovered on the bed. Carolyn just chews on a mouthful of hair as Rachel's flashlight beam explores the space. A little gasp from the fat woman as the flashlight hits Carolyn's legs.

The old man is wandering around the apartment now on his own, feeling his way through the darkness. He flips a light switch and gets nothing and then, a dull flicker and then nothing.

"Nice place," the man says to Michael.

"You know, you're stealing this place from us if you buy it."

The old man says nothing, pretends not to hear.

"So if you move in I'm just going to sneak in here one night and slit your throat and then wifey's. Then I'll plop you into the stream."

The man gets real red in the face. In the storm, physical fitness is prime. The old man is one drop of oil away from a heart explosion. He's still sweating from the walk up the stairs. Michael imagines choke-slamming the old man, right through a window.

The old couple leaves with Rachel kind of hissing.

Later, Carolyn and Michael hold each other in the silence in the kitchen. The storm is turning black. Grains of instant coffee float on the surface of two steaming mugs. There's nothing to talk about. Lyle still hasn't come.

They come apart and pick up their coffee. They find themselves moving. Michael and Carolyn walk to the window together and look down over the wet city. The streets are swirling with white and yellow foam and boats weave their way through the flotsam and jetsam that now serve as traffic. Michael presses his nose to the window and feels the deep cold of the glass. Carolyn swirls the juices around in her mouth and thinks about toothpaste. There's thunder and then claws of lightning make a dull strobe of the apartment. They finish their coffees.

"Wanna fool around?" Carolyn asks.

Frank Hinton lives in Halifax Nova Scotia and edits the online magazine *Metazen*.

SPREAD OPTION SCHEME

CAL FREEMAN

The mascot was misbehaving,
Our noble jester run amok—
She was having huge success
At the time; that is how
She put it: "huge"—
Photography doesn't require so much
An understanding of the behavior
Of light as an intuition about it—
A man taking pictures of a fountain,
A man taking a picture of a golden
Grizzly, a man taking a picture
Of a man—He must man up
And tell the grandmother the wedding
Will not take place in a church
But in another stone structure
With vaulted ceilings
And grey dovecotes, a space built
For the enjoyment of Henry and Clara
Ford, great acoustics, stained glass,
A baby grand piano that cannot
Be touched—I'm not sure why
My business students are drawn
To the Muses and Errors Fountain
In front of the campus library
(A belief that water is a commodity
That bears watching? A belief
That the aesthetics of water and light
Can be mastered?)—If only our mascot
Would keep its paws to itself, if only
He wouldn't make jerk-off signals
To the opposing crowd—I believe our school
Hungers and will devour another school—

A girl who dislikes football
Wears black to the ceremony
And makes up the necessary ground;
She could be easily mistaken for another
Stripe amidst the black and gold.

A STRUCTURALIST'S GUIDE TO SINK MAINTENANCE

CAL FREEMAN

Jerry Nichols makes a wrench sleeve from the straight piece of a drain trap. His flannel shirt sleeve brushes against the wrench sleeve while he works at ratcheting locknuts beneath a faucet head. Sleeves become sleeves and parts of sinks become parts of new sinks; parts of sinks become tools for repairing old sinks with spirited-away parts. The vectoring of the two sleeves is what the structurality of structure caused as soon as the first sink was installed. In our neighborhood the totems are transitive involving on random days sinks, squirrels, dogs, elms, brown bottles. Prohibitions against tossing out old sinks are seasonal. Prohibitions against killing squirrels are rare, however in certain instances where a dog has feared a firing gun or the police were in earshot I have known the killing of squirrels to stop. Jerry Nichols has prohibited the consumption of squirrels under any circumstance. As a retired teamster driver, he balances competing moieties: truck/dog/brown bottle/squirrel/sink/alligators of tires in the road. Squirrels are rabid. Dogs are kind. Elms feed upon an underground stream concomitant to above-ground currents. In a careful bricolage, we keep the water running down.

Cal Freeman was born and raised in west Detroit. He graduated from University of Detroit Mercy in 2002 and received his MFA from Bowling Green State University in 2004. His poems have appeared in such journals as *Rattle*, *Commonweal*, *The Journal*, *Nimrod*, *Drunken Boat*, and *Hotel Amerika*, as well as several other publications. In 2004 Terrance Hayes selected his manuscript for the Devine Poetry Fellowship, and he has also been nominated for the Pushcart Prize. He currently teaches poetry and creative writing at University of Detroit Mercy.

THE WINDOW ABOVE THE SINK

HILARY KING

Kitchens used to be built around
the window above the sink.
An everyday altar of
knickknacks and aspirin,
It let in light
and let the housewife look out
on her children safely playing,
her garden growing her laundry blowing,
the whole world rolling slowly
in and out of view.

Now everybody wants
an island in their kitchen.
Counters of shining stone,
lights that hang like diamonds
or vanish into the sky.
One computer at least and a tv
for everyone to watch
on the island.

The circus has come inside,
and our gaze followed the parade.
Distracted by appetite,
we linger less at the window
above the sink. No more
busy hands suddenly stopped
at the sight of a single backyard bird,
red-feathered and watching.

WOMEN AT THE POOL

HILARY KING

Mornings and most afternoons
The pool is a world run by women.

Gunslingers they are
In straw hats and dark glasses
Black-skirted bathing suits

Their hands a blur against the blue
They sweep their herds to the restroom
Round up the strays,
Then turn them loose by the snack bar.
Lunch.

Later, on the bench by the sandbox,
Keeping an eye on the screamer,
They relax, leaning in elbows to knees,
To compare camps and profile pictures.
Cell phones and friendship,
The handguns of modern motherhood.

Hilary King lives, writes and wanders about in Atlanta, Georgia. Her poetry has appeared in local and national publications.

PAPYRUS OF THE YELLOW-THROATED WARBLER

SHENA MCAULIFFE

DISCUSSED: Anatomy—Ancient Egypt—Betrayal—Birds—Book of the Dead—Diagram of the Heart—Dissection—Feather of Truth and Justice—Guilt—Mummification—Northern Towns—Papyrus—Scholars—Tourism—Weight

Here begin the chapters of the coming forth by day.

We were kneeling on the driveway of our rental house, our first house together, and our last. We were looking at a dead bird—small, yellow-throated and intact, tiny talons curled.

You said a bird's heart beats much faster than a human heart. Its blood races through every millimeter of its body in no time at all.

I suggested we mummify the little thing—remove its brain, a brain being useless in the Egyptian afterlife. But I got it wrong. I said the heart, too, would have to go.

No, no, you said. You shook your head. Not the heart. The heart is the only organ that stays. The heart rules the soul and the intellect. It goes with the body to the afterlife, so it can be weighed against the feather. A heavy heart is a guilty heart, and it gets eaten by Ammut, the half-crocodile, half-hippopotamus god.

No heart is lighter than a feather, I said.

Your eyes were unblinking, your beautiful eyes, a freckle in each iris. Your eyes, so light brown they could almost be called yellow. I blinked first.

Okay, you said, nudging the bird with your index finger.

For the time being, we wrapped it in a rumpled tissue you found in your pocket.

It's perfectly clean, you said, smoothing it out. It was just in case you needed it.

Let me do all the things one does on the earth, such as walking hither and thither.

The Egyptian *Book of the Dead* is also known as *Spells for Coming or Going Forth By Day*. It is full of prayers, praise hymns, instructions and pleas: for a mouth, for breath, to prevent rotting, to maintain or regain control of one's legs, to retain one's heart.

In the afterlife the heart is in continual danger of being snatched.

How, then, after all these prayers, with heart and mouth and breath intact, with legs that walk and bend and grow sore with use—how is the afterlife different from the present life? The Egyptian underworld seems to run parallel to the overworld, a separate but similar village, located beneath the soil but above the molten core.

But keep reading (you would say). There are prayers for avoiding work, for turning into a sparrow or a heron or a hawk. For turning into a water lily.

One must work in the afterlife? Cutting and cultivating the field of reeds? And who would want to be a water lily? A flower: tall and bright and beautiful, but inanimate? Your stem so long, so tangled, so far from your plumage, and all of you nourished by pond muck?

Come forth by day. Go forth by day. There are no prayers for night.

Offerings include: cakes and ale, barley-wheat, mud bricks, reeds.

Our rental house was on the lake, fronted by cedars that swarmed with mosquitoes. It was shake-shingled, painted gray and peeling. The back of the house was all glass—windows and sliding doors looked across the sand to the water. The lake was gray that day. It was often gray, even during summer. It was July; it must have been nine o' clock, but the sun hadn't set. You unlocked the front door and reached down to slap a mosquito off the back of your knee. You smashed it mid-bite and smeared blood across your skin.

I am silent.

From the right side of the heart, blood comes forth into the lungs. From the lungs, blood goes forth to the rest of the body. All day and night, the blood goes forth.

Thy right eye is like the Sektet Boat, thy left eye is like the Atet Boat.

For the mummification you covered the kitchen table with typing paper. You cut the bird's skull open with a scalpel I never knew you had. The blade was fresh. You scooped the brain out with a teaspoon, like seeds from a melon.

Useless brain, I said.

I touched your temple with my fingers, but you were busy. You brushed my hand away.

You sliced along the bird's sternum.

Why don't you prepare the bandages? you said.

I got up from the table. It was like a hospital in our kitchen—like a hospital and like a morgue. The ugly lamp hung from a chain above the table. Moths circled. Hospital. Morgue. Temple. Prison. You dropped the brain into the trash.

In town, fifteen miles north, drunks were staggering through the streets. Teenagers were necking at the swimming beach, clammy-skinned, their heads filled with cricket chirps. Cars drove up Jefferson, windows rolled down. Middle-aged couples strolled, licking ice-cream cones and doling out bite-sized pieces of fudge to their grubby children, who dropped lumps of chewing gum on the sidewalk. At that very moment, tee-shirt vendors were turning out shop lights and locking doors, stepping into the night, stretching and sighing.

You and I agreed: we hated candy apples, ice cream, fudge, and caramel corn. We hated fingernail polish and lipstick, suntans, and big, bright expensive sneakers. We hated golf pants and diamond rings.

But I have always liked the color of streetlight on a summer night. I lie awake and listen for the rising and falling of music as a car passes. When we met—remember? I lived above the shops in town, where I heard laughter and whistling and glasses clinking at all hours. Once in a while, a cigarette, or the chance of an unexpected whisper in my ear—the way the hair on my arms rises—the three little bones in my ear vibrate—the lips of the whisperer so close—but not touching me.

Dedication: Hair, lips, teeth, belly, flesh, trunk, fingers, breast, backbone, throat.

A note on the Papyrus of Hunefer: On his way to the afterlife, Hunefer is clothed in semi-translucent white. The outline of his thin, straight legs is evident through the gown. Like many Egyptians depicted on papyrus, Hunefer is androgynous but for his black goatee. He is both stiff and graceful, looking ahead, holding the hand of Inpu, the jackal god. His feet, face, and hands are drawn in profile, but his chest and shoulders face forward, like a Barbie doll gone wrong, its shoulders twisted out of line by an older sibling or a teething baby.

Hunefer, I tell you, there is no turning back. The jackal god sees through your clothes, through your skin. Your heart, after all, is no longer beating inside your chest, but is even now being lowered to the scales.

Crouched beside the scales sits Ammut: bone eater, swallower, devourer of the dead. With the hind quarters of a hippopotamus and the snout of a crocodile, she can't run very fast. Her legs are too stubby. No hunting for Ammut. She is the dog of the underworld, waiting for table scraps or rawhide, waiting for your heart. It is delivered directly to her mouth.

I am a sparrow. I am a sparrow. I am a scorpion.

Since early June, I had been taking long walks in the dark. Each night, fires burned along the beach, and there were always boys drinking beer. Sometimes they threw bottles into the flames. Once I watched a boy piss on the fire to put it out—all acrid, hissing steam. His friends were gone. He was the last one. He didn't see me, standing at the water's edge, watching. He finished and lay down on the sand, outside the ring of rocks and stumps on which the boys usually sat. He stretched out on his back and looked up at the stars and the dwindling column of smoke. I walked on.

I have dipped and washed and buried the inside parts. I have dug them up.

Buried in hot sand, a body dries quickly, though not as quickly as flesh rubbed with natron, a kind of salty soda-ash. Natron dessicates the flesh, which is then opened, the organs removed. The brain is crushed and drained through the nostrils. The body is wrapped and wrapped and tucked away. But sand and natron are not the only ways. There is ice. There is the density and acid of the peat bog.

It is air and water that damage us. All our lives we need them, but in death we are defenseless against their swarms.

Adze, chisel, little finger: open my mouth.

You pried the bird's chest open with your scalpel while I dipped linen strips in flour paste. You were wearing your glasses. They slipped down your nose and cast shadows across your cheekbones.

You already knew about Jonah. You said you'd forgive me.

You pulled out little, indistinguishable viscera.

I asked if you would bury them with the mummy, in jars.

You didn't even nod.

You knew about Jonah. You knew I had gone with him, once or twice, to the garden shack where he slept on a cot. He didn't have electricity, but he had a bowl of peaches on a rough table. He had half a bottle of red wine. He had flat, brown, thickly callused feet. He had a frayed red rug that needed to be laundered. You didn't want to know more. You said you'd forgive me, but I didn't want to be forgiven.

I have not caught fish with bait made of the bodies of the same kind of fish.

No heart is lighter than a feather, even if the heart is small and the feather large. The average adult heart weighs between nine and eleven ounces, surprisingly light, yet heavier, certainly, than the average ostrich feather. A heart—for all that muscle and protein, the ventricles and atria and various valves, the four chambers still heavy with blood—has the heft of two cups of hazelnuts, or a stick and a half of butter.

Keep from me the stinking bones.

Where are you now? Sitting at a desk, surrounded by books, a half-full glass of water condensing on a coaster within your reach? You take methodical sips. You run your fingers through your hair. It's short, I'm sure. Or even shaved, so you don't have to worry about it. I loved that about you—the minimalism: the black coffee, the undressed salad, the perfectly trimmed nails. You lean close to the copy of a papyrus pressed beneath a sheet of glass. You pause and take off your glasses to polish the lenses with the cloth you keep folded in your pocket.

I have not tampered with the plumb bob of the balance.

It was Hippocrates that taught us that the heart only beats. The heart is mere battery, while the brain is the intellect, personality, emotion, and soul. The brain became separate and superior to the body. The brain is where intangibles pulse: guilt, god, epiphany. And these? Magnetic fields flickering against the parietal temporal lobe.

I am content when I breathe his odor.

Jonah is a bartender, and a kayak guide on the lake. Paddle with a rhythm, he says. Rock a little. Sit up straight. He points out the shipwreck and how the buoy marks the channel. In September, he weatherizes summer homes. In December, he plays hockey with a broom. He runs a snow blower, clears the sidewalk in front of the restaurant with goats on the roof. He eats dandelion greens, almonds and lentils, dried fruit, day-old bagels. In the morning he sits on the step in the sun. The mosquitoes lay low when the sun is hot. Once, he let me peel a callus from the bottom of his foot.

Heart scarab, dung beetle, quiet my heart.

In ancient Egypt the sun was a dung ball rolled across the sky each day by Khperi, god of the rising sun--a dung beetle. Day after day, the beetle rolled its dung across the sky.

I have not stopped the flow of water.

Or I wanted to be forgiven, but I didn't want you to take me back. I didn't want you to kiss my closed eyelids. I didn't want to watch your chest rise and fall while you slept beneath our cheap muslin sheets. I didn't want to lie beside you, watching the sky through the bare window, listening to you breathe, until the leaves browned and fell and the trees stood bare, and the lake grew a new crust, and still the sheet over your chest rose and fell.

The bird didn't make it. When you pulled out the viscera the bones gave way. The body was empty and delicate and crushed, but you said: Do you want to see the heart? It might be lighter than a feather. It's very small.

You held it out for me to see, and pulled the chest open with the tip of scalpel. I leaned in. It was tiny, severed, just sitting in there, like a raisin.

Even as Jonah traced my clavicle with a single finger, and the hair on my arms rose, I sat perfectly still, and even then I thought of you—washing your hands and drying them, so slowly, then unrolling the papyrus onto your desk. Setting your pen down and shaking your hand to keep it from cramping. The way you sometimes mutter when you write.

Jonah said, Relax.

The lake stone I gave you, smooth and pale: your heart scarab, your paperweight. How you wanted, more than anything, to be the lake.

Shena McAuliffe's writing has appeared in *Conjunctions*, *Black Warrior Review*, *Alaska Quarterly Review* and *Cutbank*. She lives in Salt Lake City, where she is a PhD candidate in Literature and Creative Writing at the University of Utah. The italicized lines in her story are adapted from various translations of *The Egyptian Book of the Dead*.

STAIN

MATTHEW LIPPMAN

You can stain a table the way you can stain a woman,
put your polyurethane all over her arms, her breasts,
call it love
but then the whole bedroom stinks of some synthetic poison
that was not meant for this world.

At the hardware store
the beautiful man with bad teeth said
throw the brush away after you're done, quick.

So, I did, almost, before I even started
because I was afraid of what the drip would do to the grass
stain it a stain
like when I told my kid she was
insane--
that kind of blemish--
that kind of *spot.*

John Adams stained the Constitution.
Eva Perón stained the alleyways of Argentina
that had been stained by the blood of Fidel Castro
and John F. Kennedy stained the bloomers
of Marilyn Monroe.
My mother stained me and I stained her right back.
My sister was stained by a flock of seagulls named Herbert, my wife,
by a herd of buffalo called *Stomp.*

You can't get away from it
and that is why I wanted to hurl the brush away,
toss the can of Thompson's All Weather Seal
before I even got going.
Who the hell needs a picnic table anyway,
to sit at and eat the savory chicken,
the medium rare steak with the bourbon based barbeque sauce?

I figure I'd I burn the thing with one match instead,
light up the night sky
then grab my neighbor, George,
and a multi-colored quilt with a hole cut in the middle,
light a fire to make signals,
send some kind of silent-spirit love song of smoke
into the night
for the all the people to see,

I figure the best thing we could do
is to be careful.

WHY LONG ISLAND JEWS ARE THE BEST JEWS

MATTHEW LIPPMAN

Drunk Jews in Manhattan are the best kind of wild elephants
especially if they bussed themselves in from Great Neck
in their neat pink Acuras with the tinted sunroofs,
the Louis Vuitton hand bags and all that sticky hair gel.
When they walk down Madison Avenue
they fall into potholes meant for the other kinds of Jews
from the upper west side Jews
who've been living there for 80 years
on Riverside Drive Jews
because where else was there to go
when the gates of Poland-hell
slammed shut on their toes
after standing in the snow for too many years?
I watch them on Facebook.
They get naked with bottles of Michelob and red plastic cups full of cheap vodka.
They smile in drunk.
I think, *Ohmygod, Haley, get me the hell out of this computer.*
But I'm stuck right in there with a Liza and a Courtney, a Joshua and a Mordecai.
I'm glued to my people from Roslyn and Jericho who moved to Boston, Tai Pei, Brooklyn,
then came back, missed those Long Island Expressway heat waves so much
it gave them all bad skin and limp dick syndrome.
Oh, if you are a drunk Jew in Idaho you gotta get your ass back to Old Westbury
so your overmedicated member, your powerful perky nipples
stay stiff, solid, and fully anchored.

You get your ass back to that long skinny island off of New York City
that is a painted fingernail in the eye
of a bohemian in Brooklyn
and you stick around.
Hell, I'm in my car right now
headed home
to drink the magic kosher Kool-Aid
that will set us all free
even though there is nowhere left to go—
the Danube, the Rhine, the river of gold stars
that slowly dries up and has no more name.

Matthew Lippman's newest collection, *MONKEY BARS*, is published by Typecast Publishing. His first book of poems, *THE NEW YEAR OF YELLOW*, is published by Sarabande Books. He lives in Boston.

WHY I HATE TEACHING

RUTH HOBERMAN

There's always someone in the class who's lost an arm
and when you tell some joke that hinges on an amputated limb,
he waves his empty sleeve grimacing, or some girl,
raped the night before, who sobs when a kid insists
the girl in the Oates story could have just said no.
There's always the one you worry will kill himself
and the other one who does but not till later,
if you're lucky, in someone else's class. Burn
the words in my forehead: I'll never know enough.

PERIPHERAL VISION

RUTH HOBERMAN

My father's bones behind my face,
his eyes behind my eyes, his shadows
hollowing my skin, glimpsed then gone

on humid days, fruit flies hang like dancing ash
over apples in my kitchen, but when I reach
my hand closes on air

Ruth Hoberman teaches twentieth century British literature at Eastern Illinois University. She has published poetry in the *Spoon River Poetry Review*, *Iron Horse Literary Review*, and *Natural Bridge*.

MOSTLY, SHE PRACTICES FALLING

KERRIN MCCADDEN

And it is true that we are incredibly lonely.
That man walking the sidewalks of your town
with a tangle of bicycle innertubes
over his shoulder like a map of his heart,
running errands, studying a nest of bowls
in a shop window, which is also like a map
of his heart, may tell you he has given up on love.
It is the way he can go home and make rice
and sit with a book and not care that he is alone.
He says he has given up on love. He practices
saying this. What is true is that I have figured out
how to do it, how to live alone. I sponge off
the table, wash the plates, and go to bed.
Sometimes there is a dog. Sometimes
an extra blanket, which is a map as well,
folded and unfolded as needed, showing
the borders of one body within the state
lines of the bed. I am the marker—*you are here*.
The rest of the bed shows what we call
up north *the flats*. This is the topography of rest.
I am in my car. The woman on the radio
talks about wanting to feel the most
intense physical sensation she can.
Instead of dancing, she practices falling.
She wants to make moves she can't help
but complete—mostly, she practices falling.
How far can she fall and not get hurt?
She wishes there were a way to measure
the intensity of pain. Before she dies, she wants
to feel it all. How far can a person fall onto a mat
and not die? This is the topography of grief.
Where is the edge of the heart, is what we want
to know. We are not afraid of words, we say.

All we can do is draw lines we cannot cross.
The words on the page are cursive,
the innertubes of thought we build into
what fine things we wish for, the trajectory
of our falling bodies, the edges of what we can say,
the things we say to the night. Once, I held
a chicken in my hands. I held its wings
to its sides. Its feet dangled like the stems
of letters. There was no heft to it, just a cage
of bones. Just a cage of bones and feathers.
Just a house of air, craning its head toward
knowing something, staring into the middle
distance, suddenly calm. This is all I know.

HOW TO MISS A MAN

KERRIN MCCADDEN

Breathing is just a rhythm. Tell yourself this so that the breathing
becomes a song. Sing this song all day while you shop in the hardware
store for things you do not need. Sing it again while you cook supper

for yourself. Cook supper for yourself, even if you don't want to.
Go for a walk, even if you don't want to. Put your shoes on
and get the leash and even bring the dog. She will be so pleased

you might start to forget. Also, breathe. It is a rhythm. Walk
around the block, and even farther, if you have a mind to.
You might. Your feet will take you. They can. If you listen,

they are a rhythm also. Like drums. Hand drums. Swing your hands
while you walk. Tell yourself they are kind of like wings,
that the bird's wing has a hand inside it. It does.

Come home and make tea. Every time you dip the teabag,
hold your breath like you are underwater. Hold. Breathe.
Hold. Breathe. Like that, like you are swimming across

Lake Pleiades, under water like a fish, above water like a bird
until you are stitching lake and sky. You are a needle just then,
darning holes in things, a weave of stitches across and down, like a graph.

You need to be a graph. A grid. Numbers are perfect. You can draw
two lines on a graph that can never touch. This is what you are building.

SAFETY INSTRUCTIONS

KERRIN MCCADDEN

Unless directed by a crew member,
do not construct if/then scenarios
—not about the plane, not about your life.
Unless directed by a crew member,
do not build flow charts for the past.
Do not sweeten your silence. Or the
beauty of the shoeshine man, who only
wanted your money. Do not consider
Denver in the rain. Unless directed
by a crew member, do not study the grid
of the western plains. The forked
and dissipating rivers do not translate.
They should not call to mind the footprints
of birds in the dust in your village. Unless
directed by a crew member, again, do not
study the western plains. Sometimes the fields
are crop circles, but these hold no mystery.
They are the elegant drawings, only, of rolling
gantries. When resting, do not lean on the man
next to you. Like the pilot, he will only talk to you
when you are making your descent into Chicago.
He will suddenly come alive, stop looking
out the window only to close the shade again quickly,
will ask his flutter of questions, then disappear.
Unless directed by a crew member, do not look
at the reading material of the men flanking you.

Do not show them the word they are searching for
is backward and diagonal. Do not reach over
and circle it. Unless directed by a crew member,
do not dream, in general, of men, or, in particular,
of one. You are suspended above the world,
a careening impossibility. You are flying, headlong.
As you fly East, the rivers are not isolated birdprints,
are a pulse. The forests return, dispatches from
the body. Unless directed by a crew member do not
calculate the weight of pronouns spoken by men.

Kerrin McCadden's poems have appeared in *American Poetry Review*, *Hunger Mountain*, *RATTLE*, *Poet Lore* and others. She was a finalist for the 2010 Ruth Stone Poetry Prize and a semi-finalist for the ""Discovery""/Boston Review 2010 Poetry Contest, the 2010 Ralph Nading Hill Award and the 2009 RATTLE Poetry Prize. She was also nominated for Best New Poets 2010. She has a residency coming up at the Vermont Studio Center. Kerrin teaches creative writing at Montpelier High School and is on the poetry faculty at The New England Young Writers' Conference at Bread Loaf. She lives in Plainfield, Vermont. Also, she has a poodle. And a family.

TARGET GIRL

SARA LIPPMANN

My boyfriend is right. When my father packs in his knives where will that leave me?

I am his Target Girl.

We are an unlikely pair. My father is a storefront minister. His faith is nondenominational. Weddings, funerals, hospice visits, he'll snap on a collar for anyone who needs a prayer. I'm barely passing trigonometry.

At night he becomes my Blade Master.

We've had a great run. Our family gig is a hit. We perform in community college auditoriums, at men's clubs, rotary clubs, for VFWs, we latch onto whatever local sideshow has rolled into town. We'll even do senior centers. Sometimes he straps me to a board like the kind used in pool safety at the Y. Other times I pose astride a large log round. Freestanding, like my mom once did. See, I may have been born into the business but I wouldn't change it.

Target girls get to dress up as if it were Halloween. I wear doilies and a duster, satin bunny ears; I have been Mae West, Pocohantas, a flapper, a nurse, whatever my father brings home. When you throw in the wigs they add up. Tonight's was long and black with rich purple waves for Wonder Woman. Plated gold cuffs on the wrists. Leotards can creep up the sides but they help Blade Master see what to hit.

His record is 80 throws per minute.

Target girls do not startle or flinch. That you learn early. When the blades start flying I widen my eyes. My brows I've plucked razor thin; it's a nervous tic but the braces have paid off. My smile is an inspiration. He's my dad! He's scraped before but never broken through skin.

My boyfriend has ideas. Think big, he'll say with a mouthful of hoagie. He's a slicer at the WaWa in Germantown Pike. He rounds up when he serves me. Slaps meat on a scale. Hey, what if I managed you?

When I get home, my father walks outside.

We have a satellite dish nailed to an easel in our backyard. Neighbors believe he's an avid archer. His are no ordinary knives. They are not pared, serrated, meant for a bird. Nothing you'd find in a block. My father throws spikes, beil-axes, Norse hawks, 64-inch spears, Allentown steel points. During target practice we are the only two in the world. No one can come between us. I assist, round up bowies that have bounced off and fallen on the grass, yank out the blades that have stuck. Each handle is a continuous sheet of metal from the tip down, cool in my hands, an even distribution of weight. I buff and I shine with the edge of my sweatshirt. He runs through spins and rotations. When he's ready for me I stand in. In that moment I want nothing more. This is the rhythm: half, one, two, and three-turn throws but by dusk the chill's come through and afterward there's homework, dinner.

We neither hide nor advertise although my mom thinks we flaunt it. People see what they want and sometimes that's double but sole service to God cannot pay. Remember the North Philly rabbi who moonlighted as a private investigator? My boyfriend thinks we could land the nightly news, too. A minister in the impalement arts? It's a modern day binding of Isaac! Putty in the bag, mom says, thrusts my boyfriend a plate.

My boyfriend booked the Trocadero. It's our biggest venue yet. Maybe he should have asked for permission but still; you'd think my dad would be happy. Tonight when he, I mean, when Blade Master parted the velvet curtain dressed like a prom date, red tie and cummerbund, black tails and spectator shoes, and took me by the hand, I knew he felt something else beneath the stage lights.

The first part of the show was routine. I stretched my arms like a tree and clasped my palms chapel tight while Blade Master had at me. Ear, ear, foot, foot. I whistled Lynda Carter's theme song. We swapped blindfolds like always. He clipped my neck. Pinned me in the armpit, right between the legs. A thousand eyes blinked. And then, the rush of applause.

That is the beauty of shock and awe.

Lately, my father is crying. I'll stand at the screen door and he'll sniff, how about a throw, pumpkin? My A-Number-One? There's a seed in his tooth. He'll twirl his knife like a baton but I won't feel like it. Or I will but *Gossip Girl*'s on or I've got a text or there's a honk in the driveway.

It's his enlarged prostate, mom says. She puts on her oven mitt, speaks to the roast she's been basting. Looks like Blade Master's sprung a leak.

After intermission he brings out the Veiled Wheel of Death. The pulley drags along the Victorian floor like a bum leg. I admit I'm surprised. We have never practiced this stunt but I trust Blade Master completely. He performed it in the 80s with my mom who no longer comes to events. Everyone's watching. I climb in the pocket between two cut sheaths as I'd seen on the clips. Slip my hands and feet through the holds. Inside the Veiled Wheel of Death Blade Master cannot see me. I spin and I spin, I am a child at Space Camp, I could squeeze water from Mars as his knives whiz by; while I spin, I think about flesh and blood. It's easier than it looks. A wheel is symmetrical. If he can do darkness, what then is motion? Blade Master follows his formula. Between paper sheets I listen. The beats knock and I know he won't miss. Sure enough, when he strips the cover and I step out intact, the air shoots out of the room.

It's a standing ovation. There must be 500 people, the sound a stampede. I throw up my arm for Blade Master. We call it the Vanna White but he's already left me. I stab a pinochle card; dangle it like a toasted marshmallow under his nose. How can he not see that I'm bursting? Sweat sits on his lip. When we curtsy and bow he barely moves. I swear something's running down his leg.

My father keeps carnival posters in the basement, adhesive crusted and dry along the wood paneling. Lithograph prints, red yellow black blotted ink. Starting to peel. Before I got into knives my father used to let me play down there with him. He'd tell stories of fire breathers and bearded ladies. God's children, he'd say, though my mother prefers the word freak. Truth is, he threw indoors until she found him viable outside targets.

Backstage tonight, my boyfriend says, keep the wig on. He tugs but it's not my real hair. Whaddya say. Let's take this show on the road.

Life is too short to play it safe. I wait in the wings for my father. He carries his knives around in a trunk as if they were for sale. Every prop must be inspected before it's stored or replaced. Tonight he takes forever so we start things and by we I mean my boyfriend. I guess it's all part of growing up. With Blade Master lost in Genesis danger finds me regardless. I wipe my mouth on my cape. A person can go crazy just hanging around. Vegas, I tell my boyfriend. Foxwoods. Atlantic City. New York, New York.

I've been honing my aim.

Sara Lippmann is a freelance writer and editor. Her fiction has appeared in places like *Our Stories*, *BLIP* (formerly *Mississippi Review*), *Potomac Review*, *Word Riot*, *Slice*, *Storyglossia*, *NANO Fiction*, *Big Muddy*, and elsewhere. It has also been included in *Sex Scene: An Anthology*, *Mamas & Papas* (City Works Press), and two other anthologies from Wising Up Press. She is a graduate of the New School's MFA program and lives in Brooklyn with her family.

THE FAT MAN'S WIFE

KATIE MOORE

I am the fat man's third wife.
El gordo. Panzon!
I was forever being
crushed beneath
the mountain of his lusts,
women and brush strokes ,
the revolution.
They say
it was like an elephant
married to a dove.
Imagine, me,
a dove!
Ridículo!
I am a brighter
plumed bird.

I am like Mexico.
It is a loud sadness,
one that smiles big with teeth,
drinks, dances, shrills
and stomps, whirling.
I wear colorful costumes
to *máscara de mi dolor*,
my skeleton is held together
by metal, and machines,
stitches, surgeons. I paint
myself in pieces and intact.
I paint the pain. I trap it
on my canvas
and make a face, stick out
my tongue. I paint myself
hairy like a little monkey.

I am beautiful, and hairy
like a little monkey.

He is like the world
I longed to see. It's not
the place to live
in peace. He is like
a revolution, a people
marching inside a person.
He can't be still, and it's not
his hands that do
the devil's work. It's the paint
and the *pinga*.
We connected
my Mexico to his world.
The bridge is built of love.
It's a small bridge.

Katie Moore is a founding editor of *The Legendary*, an upstart little mag where words are God and God is a dirty old man. She lives in Memphis with two pit bulls, two daughters, and one cop. The cop is either her husband or a secret agent assigned to protect the world from her manic schemes. Find Katie, and her publication credits, online at The Girl Circus, www.thegirlcircus.com.

ABNORMAL TIDES

TIM KAHL

The North Sea, owing to its shape, is subject to dangerous
surges. The tide there is an influence to escape from.

A sudden change of wind direction generates waves
that wash away the shore of Holland, and off the shore

of Ireland the clefts and troughs are older injuries,
the heavy work of glaciers. The sediment is ordered

by the extremes of weather, by the continuous flow
of salt through an organism that's diurnal.

By day the shallow water urges the explorers.
At night the sea is merely a theory of currents,

a consistent churn of waves that reach their ideal in
deeper water, in the past's pressures.

The surge comes when it is least expected,
with fast-moving storm conditions

that blow over power lines and knock down fences.
I live where this whole system opens,

where its purpose waits to ride in us. I live for
its inescapable anomalies, its furious progressions,

the lines of the moraine it issues and records in me.
Inside, the asymmetry, the crags and impressions.

The canyons can be traced far out onto
the abyss of the North Sea plains.

Tim Kahl, www.timkahl.com, is the author of *Possessing Yourself* (Word Tech, 2009). His work has been published in *Prairie Schooner*, *Indiana Review*, *Ninth Letter*, *Notre Dame Review*, *The Journal*, *Parthenon West Review*, and many other journals in the U.S. He appears as Victor Schnickelfritz at the poetry and poetics blog The Great American Pinup, greatamericanpinup.wordpress.com/, and the poetry video blog Linebreak Studios, linebreakstudios.blogspot.com/. He is also editor of Bald Trickster Press and is the vice president and hosting coordinator of The Sacramento Poetry Center. He currently teaches at The University of the Pacific.

PINK BALLERINAS

KATHLEEN HELLEN

It's Degas but it isn't. A forgery of pink chiffon and ballerinas. A cheap reproduction I loved. It's you but it isn't. A long time ago. Dancing in your slippers with pink ribbons cinched at ankles. A costumed brilliance in the mirror. Long legs, long fingers. The curved pale of your throat. The shocking glimpse of nipple when you lifted your shirt. A berry in the milk, not dark like mine, although we seemed in every other way (size, demeanor) identical. The fit of a glass slipper. A kiss like kissing myself. The whisper of your gown those nights I stayed over. Curtains drawn. The narrow bed, the tight little room. The walls hung with pink ballerinas.

Kathleen Hellen's work has appeared in *Barrow Street*, *Cimarron Review*, *The Cortland Review*, the *Hollins Critic*, *Nimrod*, *Prairie Schooner*, *Salamander*, *Southern Poetry Review*, *Subtropics*, *Witness*, among others. Awards include the Washington Square Review, James Still and Thomas Merton poetry prizes, as well as individual artist grants from Maryland and the city of Baltimore. Her chapbook *The Girl Who Loved Mothra* from Finishing Line Press is listed on amazon.com. She is a contributing editor for the *Baltimore Review*.

EL PUEBLO VENCERÁ

JAMES WINTER

Argentina, 1977

Beatriz heard them pull up to her house. Her husband, Adelmo, did not stir. He slept soundly, his stink filling the room. She heard truck doors open and shut, and men talk in hushed voices below her bedroom window. Beatriz looked at the watercolor portrait of the Savior hung above her headboard and prayed for Him to drive the men away. He usually watched over her with warmth and caring, but that night He had lifeless, empty eyes.

Over the past year, whenever Beatriz heard these men whispered about at her diner counter, she dismissed them as mere stories and gossip. Articles about the men did not appear in the newspapers. The radio did not broadcast these horror stories nor were they reported on the evening news. Who was to say they had taken place?

But as these stories moved closer to San Miguel, Beatriz grew afraid. Mr. Rizian, a former suitor of one of Beatriz's high school girlfriends, left the paper mill one Sunday and was not heard from again. Rita, the bright girl who managed the summer market, disappeared from her apartment. The previous autumn, Luciana's son was snatched from his bed. Luciana, Beatriz's best short-order cook, quit work and now lived in Salta with her sister.

On Christmas the men came to Beatriz's neighborhood and took Eva Numez's girls. Numez's shrieking brought the entire neighborhood outside to see what had happened. When Beatriz realized what did, she counted her blessings and went back to bed.

Still, Beatriz never truly believed the men would come for her family. She and Adelmo ran a barely profitable diner. Their oldest son, Ignacio, a philosophy major at NU Cuyo, was by no means the sharpest boy of his class. Their oldest daughter, Marcena, had not yet graduated high school. Their baby boy, Pichi, could not yet sit up. The men had no reason to come here.

But they had.

Beatriz sat up in bed when she heard the men march up her front stairs.

Then it sounded as if her front door exploded.

Beatriz was already on her feet and in the living room when the men invaded her home. One grabbed her by her hair and clubbed her to her knees. He kicked her in the stomach until she doubled over, screaming. He put his boot to her back and pressed her to the floor. She craned her neck, everything in her body afire, and looked toward the bedroom hallway.

Adelmo stood there, gripping the walls. Stamping his bare feet, he gave a high-pitched shout and charged the men. A baton lashed, lifting her husband off his feet. Stumbling like a drunk, he fell face-first to the floor. As one of the men slipped a black bag over Adelmo's head and handcuffed his wrists behind his back, Beatriz saw the man was in uniform. He wore high boots and jungle fatigues. He was a soldier.

A soldier knelt near Beatriz, stabbed the couch, and spilled its stuffing. He examined the cushions, yelled "Nada," and then stabbed the recliner. Beatriz heard another soldier smashing plates in the kitchen. A third one, the one who'd assaulted Adelmo, went down the hallway to the back bedrooms and Beatriz heard her children scream.

A man behind her barked an order and the soldiers who'd been pinning her to the floor and destroying her furniture jogged down the bedroom hallway after their comrade.

Beatriz got to her knees and looked at the fifth and final soldier at her front door.

He was undoubtedly the commanding officer. Numerous stripes and bars were sewn on the collar of his shirt and he had a white cross pinned to his red beret. He was handsome. Thumbs hooked in his belt loops, his tall frame stood ramrod straight. He had a square jaw and a block-head, but a thin nose and high cheek bones dotted with pockmarks.

The officer's eyes darted toward the bedroom hallway, where there came the sounds of a scuffle, but they came back to her as she knelt there, trying to catch her breath. She thought he pitied her, so she leapt to her feet and grabbed his uniform front and pleaded, "Don't do this. Don't do this."

He pushed her and she tripped. As she fell, she saw him stop himself from reaching out to catch her.

She heard a man cry, "Damn it," from the back bedrooms.

There came a gunshot.

Beatriz lay frozen, her mouth open. She dug her fingernails into the floorboards.

One of the soldiers dragged Ignacio from the back bedrooms. He wore only white briefs with the black bag over his head. He was fat; everything on him jiggled as he struggled against the handcuffs. Another solider followed, cradling baby Pichi. Pichi screeched and kicked his legs. The solider whispered, "Shhh, child. Everything is fine. No tears, please."

The soldiers brought their quarries to the commanding officer. Beatriz reached for Ignacio. The soldier holding Pichi kicked her. She held her side, weeping, and called to Adelmo.

"I'm here, honey. I'm here," he croaked through the black bag.

Beatriz watched the soldiers take Ignacio and Pichi down the front steps and out of sight.

The last two soldiers came into the living room, one pressing his hand to a bloody gash on his shoulder. The other holstered his pistol and said to the commanding officer, "Little bitch stabbed Alomar."

"Get in the truck," the officer told them.

The soldier with the pistol snatched Adelmo off the floor by his manacled wrists and pushed him toward the front door.

"Fucking pigs!" Adelmo cried. "Goddamned sons of whores. Goddamned cowards."

The soldier kicked Adelmo's feet from under him.

"Shut up," he ordered. "It'll be easier for you."

"Fuck your mother!" Adelmo bellowed.

Beatriz watched the soldier hoist Adelmo to his feet and throw him down the front stairs. Screaming, she hurried on her hands and knees to the front window and saw her husband lying on the sidewalk. The soldier hustled to Adelmo, baton held high, and struck his head until it bounced off the pavement like a fútbol.

"Stop," the officer barked to his man. "Victor, stop!"

With a sly grin, Victor put away his baton. He dragged Adelmo to the humvee parked on the street and tossed his body in the back of it. Beatriz heard her children screaming inside the humvee. Victor stepped into the back of it and closed its doors. All was silent.

The commanding officer jogged down the front steps, but stopped midway to look at Beatriz through the living room window streaked with previous washings and flecks of dirt. He looked at her almost as if he wished to apologize for the inconvenience he'd caused. The front stoop light came on at the house across the street. Its sudden brightness blinded Beatriz, and by the time the light went out, the officer and the humvee were gone.

■

She stared out the front window, cotton-mouthed, surrounded by upholstery stuffing. The soldiers did not return for her. The night dragged on.

Though Beatriz watched the sun peek above the houses across the street, she did not see the dawn. She did not see her neighbors crowded at her front door. She did not see her sister arrive or feel her take her by her shoulders and lead her to bed. Instead, her world flickered like a movie skipping frames, like at the Cine de la Luz, where she, Adelmo, and their children spent so much time giggling at Harpo's faces and at Chico's fingers tumbling over piano keys.

The Cine de la Luz had been their favorite spot in San Miguel before the government closed it. Beatriz's family loved Westerns. Ignacio had become fascinated with John Wayne at a young age. He mimicked his drawl and hefty, surefooted stance wherever he went. He'd waltz into his parents' bedroom and say, "Well…what're you makin'…for dinner?" Beatriz and Adelmo would laugh and applaud and Ignacio would waltz back out of the room and return for another performance.

Beatriz dreamed of Ignacio. In her dream, her son leaned against her bedroom doorjamb and did his John Wayne impression, but she couldn't hear him. There were too many people talking in the room, yet when Beatriz told them to shut up they only talked louder. Finally, Ignacio turned and went back down the hall, his shoulders slumped and head hanging.

■

Beatriz slept late the following morning, and started her day like any other. Groaning, her hands pressed to her sides, she knelt at the foot of her bed and prayed. Her sister came in with a cup of tea and pleaded for her to get back in bed. Ignoring her, Beatriz went to Marcena's bedroom.

Marcena's slim body had been wrapped in white sheets. Her bedding had been stripped and her pillow turned over. A smudged brown-red streak covered the wall by the open window.

Beatriz took one step into the room. Her sister moaned, "Oh, Bea, I—"

"Where is it?" Beatriz whispered.

"What?"

"The knife she used to stab the man."

"It doesn't matter."

Beatriz hissed, "Cecili—." Sharp pains in her sides choked her.

Cecilia reached into the folds of her dress and handed it to Beatriz: a butter knife.

Handing the knife back to Cecilia, Beatriz hurried out of the house.

She went in the small cubby beneath the front stairs and came out with Ignacio's bicycle. He had ridden it home from NU Cuyo that May. Beatriz managed to swing one leg over the seat before she started shaking.

Ignacio had scratched "El Pueblo Vencerá" on the handlebars. She had told him not to. Someone was bound to report him. The wire basket behind the seat still held his college textbooks, protest pamphlets their bookmarks. She had demanded he throw them away. He told her he had. He'd lied. Pichi had lain in that basket two days earlier and Ignacio had pedaled them up and down the street, Pichi squealing with delight. How could Ignacio put his brother in this basket while ignoring her warnings? Didn't he realize what he'd bring upon them? Beatriz got off the bicycle and pushed it from her. It rolled a few meters before it wobbled and fell.

Putting her hands to her face, she whispered, "Sorry, Ignacio." She righted the bike and put it back in the cubby beneath the stairs.

"Come back inside," Cecilia called from the front steps. "Please. Come back inside."

Ashamed at how she'd treated Ignacio's bicycle, Beatriz refused. She turned from her sister and looked at her neighborhood. The houses were similar: two-story concrete squares with dented aluminum front doors and chipped slate roofs, their eaves hung with bright flower baskets. Only Eva Numez's home was different. Her yard was brown, her flowers wilted.

Beatriz stepped toward Numez's house and cold water stung her feet. She looked up the sidewalk and saw water running from under a pile of soaked newspapers. It flowed past her front stairs and washed down a sewer grate near the curb. She went to the newspapers, threw them aside, and found the source: a garden hose, Mr. Leon's, her next door neighbor. The mustached old man appeared from behind the potted shrubs at his front door, his hands in his pockets. He barely met her gaze. Scowling, she dropped the hose and turned from him. Then she saw dark spots on the sidewalk and knew Mr. Leon had been trying to wash away Adelmo's blood.

Trembling, Beatriz saw families watching her through their front windows. Once more the world flickered, its frames skipped. Beatriz felt light-headed, but when she saw her sister crying on her front stairs, this dizziness left her. She went to Cecilia, took her hand, and said, "Let's have breakfast."

■

The undertaker laid Beatriz's daughter in a rough pine box and they buried her on Esperanza Hill. Beatriz refused to spend family savings on a plot in San Miguel's Catholic cemetery. Cecilia rebuked her, but Beatriz countered: "I need that money. Travel is not cheap." So, she had a small, quiet funeral for Marcena. Daniel Salazar, defrocked priest and neighborhood handyman, read from Job at the graveside.

Dr. Quintana came later that week with a chest compress, gauze, and explicit instructions for Beatriz not to get out of bed or go back to work at the diner. One broken rib was dangerously close to her lung. "The NRO took my David for treating one escapee," Dr. Quintana said, stuffing her medical supplies in a little black bag, "but he's not dead. I remember him."

The next day, ignoring the sharp pains in her side that brought nausea whenever she breathed, Beatriz rode Ignacio's bicycle to the town police station. It was a one-floor brick building behind a rusty chain-link fence, its gate always open. Inside, there was no one at the front desk. She called "Hola?" until Chief Braulio appeared. Fat, sweaty, Braulio fidgeted with a set of keys on his belt loop as he came toward her and embraced her. Braulio and Adelmo had been close friends. Their children had played together before the Braulios moved to a neighborhood uptown.

Beatriz began to speak, but Braulio told her, "I don't know."

"You do," Beatriz said. "They come here for names and addresses." She bit the inside of her cheek to keep from shouting. "They come to you."

"They tell me nothing," he said.

"You tell them everything. They must tell you where they take—"

Braulio sighed. "Bea, my family—"

She spit on the gold star pinned to his chest and left.

■

That summer Beatriz searched San Miguel and the surrounding province of Tucuman for her family. She rode Ignacio's bicycle over hills and trails, only sometimes darting through city streets and busy squares. Mostly she stuck to back roads and never moved at night. Her ribs pained her. She knew they were not healing, but she did not care.

She put photographs of her family, black-and-white headshots cut from the pictures in the bedroom hall, in Adelmo's money clip. The clip was a golden donkey's head, buck-toothed and smiling, a joke from her to Adelmo on their fifteenth wedding anniversary. When Adelmo laughed, he snorted and honked, his wide upper teeth jutting over his lower. She and the children always gave him a hard time about it, Marcena most of all. She'd mimic her father's laugh and it would then become a game between her and Ignacio of who did the best impression, her of their father versus his of John Wayne. Beatriz wore the money clip on a silver chain around her neck and kept it inside her dress. As she pedaled Ignacio's bicycle, the cold metal tapped at her breast.

Beatriz first checked the hospitals, pictures in hand. She refused to leave until someone answered her. Doctors did not. Instead, they nodded to nurses, who shook their heads and said, "We've seen nobody, had nobody by those names. Sorry, senora."

Then Beatriz went to the police stations, but never alone. She waited to go inside them with groups of strangers. The police, like Chief Braulio, could not be trusted.

Policemen wouldn't answer her either. She overheard them groan from back offices, "Another mother? My God, send her away." Always the secretaries had the duty of frowning and telling her, "Sorry, senora."

Finally she went to the churches, the ultimate refuge for those who escaped the death squads. Yet churchmen in silk robes and gold rings only offered her forgiveness and salvation, never an answer, never a place to turn.

"Forgive," the Father at San Miguel told her, motioning to the pews of praying mothers. "Ask Him to protect your family, wherever they are. Pray for hope."

"I do."

"Then what more is there to seek?"

■

Dr. Quintana advised, "Go back to work. It might ease the pain," and at the New Year, Beatriz reopened the family diner.

Beatriz prayed for the strength to forget her family. Dwelling on what the NRO might be doing or have done to them was driving her insane. She would not give the NRO, if they even cared she existed, the satisfaction of breaking her. Although she'd contemplated suicide, what had saved her was her hope of finding her family. After six months of searching, that hope seemed lost. If she could not find them, she wanted to be rid of their memory. It was too much of a cross to bear. So, she vowed never to be like Eva Numez, who sat home alone so beaten by her loss she wasted whatever life she had left.

Her diner reopened to two kinds of people: those who avoided her and those who ate quietly and left generous tips. She could stand neither.

That spring did not pass quickly. It was the season of Pichi's birth.

On what would've been Pichi's second birthday, Beatriz turned off the diner's lights, locked the front door, and flipped the sign on the door to "Closed." Sitting at the counter, she wept for lacking the strength to forget Pichi and her family.

Months passed. The summer seemed endless. The rag Ignacio had used to wipe the counters stayed dry in its porcelain dish by the sinks. She let none of her staff touch it.

June turned into July. It had been a year since they'd been taken, a year since Adelmo had shouted, "I got it, Bea," after she called an order to the kitchen, a year since Pichi had opened his chocolate eyes to the morning and woke them all.

Autumn hit San Miguel in a harsh blast of wind and rain. Beatriz found herself working at the diner more. She covered her waitress' shifts no matter their excuses. She stayed later to clean the counters one last time. She even began opening on Sundays. One Sunday, as a customer chatted callously with her about the NRO as if her family had not been taken, she remembered what her grandmother said to her mother when she had told her family she was leaving Beatriz's father for a younger man. "Women who forget their families aren't women." As Beatriz filled more of her time with work, she wondered what her grandmother would think of her.

Walking home from work on the Day of the Dead, Beatriz stopped at Eva Numez's house. She crept up Numez's front stairs and peeked in her living room window. A lone candle burned inside. Beside it, asleep in a rocking chair, was Numez. Although she was only four years older than Beatriz, she looked like a crone. Her chin rested on her chest, her graying hair wiry and tangled. Both hands were folded in her lap, and in them she clutched a ragged purple scarf.

That night, like every night, Beatriz prayed. She glared at her watercolor portrait of the Savoir and demanded He assure her she never became like Numez. She asked for forgiveness for trying to forget her family and wanted to know what she should do. She awaited His reply. The watercolor's creamy, rosy-cheeked face remained expressionless. He had those empty, lifeless eyes again. But when the night quieted and dreams overtook her, Beatriz heard an answer, not from the heavens, but from inside: she had to know where they were. She had the right to know.

■

Beatriz began searching outside Tucuman. She hired neighborhood men who'd been laid off from the American clothing factories to cover her shifts at the diner. She assured them she'd only be gone on weekends. Soon, however, weekends turned to weeks as she went north to Jujuy, across the mountains to the high rises of Misiones, and south to Santa Cruz's cold tip. No matter the province, whether from the mouths of nurses, secretaries, or barroom rebels who claimed to have heard a rumor, Beatriz endured, "Sorry, senora."

She spent most of her money on bus fares. Soon, with only enough money left in her bank account to buy food, she resorted to riding Ignacio's bicycle once more.

That winter outside of Catamarca, a beat-up sedan ran her off the road. Beatriz abandoned the bicycle and jumped in the ditch. When she recovered her breath and the car had sped away, she found Ignacio's bicycle mangled in the opposite lane. She left it near the ditch and hitchhiked back to San Miguel.

Not having the will to work the diner, she sold it for a small sum to three Rosario businessmen. She had decided to leave San Miguel. Having grown tired of fiddling with the body of the snake, she wanted to go to its heart: Buenos Aires.

Her sister stopped by the morning Beatriz intended to leave. While Beatriz packed a knapsack of food and drink, Cecilia came into her kitchen and said, "I got something for you." She laid a length of white cloth on the stove. "I took it from Marcena's burial sheets. Just felt like something I should do. You should have it."

Beatriz thanked and embraced her sister.

"There's no changing your mind?" Cecilia asked.

"No."

"You can live with me and Pablo. You have nieces and nephews."

Beatriz shook her head. "I don't have my family. I've tried to forget and I can't."

"You can't leave it be? How can you hope to make the NRO listen?"

"I don't know. But I can't keep living like this. I have to know."

"And if they turn you away, will you come home?"

Beatriz nodded. Cecilia took her to the bus station and paid her fare. They said their goodbyes. As the bus pulled out of the station, Beatriz didn't dare look out the window at her sister. If she did, she might never leave.

■

It looked just like the pictures of the American capitol building in her elementary school books. Made of white marble, parts of it streaked with green and flecks of brown and black, the Capital Federal rose above the Plaza de Mayo. Beatriz stood in its shadow, the morning sun blocked by the lime-green dome with its bronze Lady Liberty pointing to the distance behind her.

A tall iron fence topped with barbed wire surrounded the Capital. Beatriz gripped it and peered through its bars. Between the fence and building were rows of palm trees, budding flower gardens, and government officials going to and from various vehicles. Guards dressed in blue and white walked the grounds, rifles on their shoulders. They were big men, well fed, young.

Beatriz turned away and walked to the center of the Plaza, weaving between hoarse-throated vendors and tourists with their cameras clicking and beggars with Styrofoam cups so used to being ignored they did not bother to ask for change. She leaned against the base of the Pirámide de Mayo, the two-hundred foot white obelisk that commemorated her country's independence from Spain. It, too, had a Lady Liberty atop it. This one looked down on the Plaza, its expression calm, reserved, somehow wiser.

Beatriz took a wax-paper bundle from her knapsack and unwrapped it. Sitting against the Pirámide, she put the wrapping aside and ate the last slices of a loaf of bread.

To the east, behind the Casa Rosada, heavy morning traffic echoed from Bolívar Street. Regarding the Rosada, the three-story brick compound where the NRO's most powerful kept their offices, Beatriz felt she no longer had the strength to climb its fence, find the monster Videla, and demand to see her family. She looked at her calloused palms and turned them over. Thin veins lined the backs of her hands. Her knuckles were wrinkled. Her feet were sore. She was tired. Everything on her body sagged, pulling at her aching knees and back, clinging to her tender ribs. She suddenly felt how old she was.

She studied the Plaza's buildings. They had seen women like her come and go. Faced with the enormity of this history, and with the anonymity of her situation, Beatriz longed for home. Old, alone, she sat in the Capital's shadow, defeated.

Across the Plaza, between a bronze monument of a general on horseback and a new American café was an old phone booth. "Cecilia," Beatriz muttered as her bread scratched its way down her throat.

She sat there a long time, weeping.

A bell rang in the Catedral Metropolitana on the western side of the Plaza. A line of statue saints stood on either side of its doors, their arms out. They looked as if they begged her to rise. She looked at the Lady Liberty atop the Pirámide. Staring down at her, it seemed to ask: "Well?"

Beatriz got to her feet. She took the white cloth Cecilia had given her from her back pocket. It still smelled of Marcena's greasy hair and knock-off American perfume. Beatriz tied it around her head in a bonnet, hauled herself onto the base of the Pirámide, and reached into her dress. She held the pictures from Adelmo's golden money clip aloft and began chanting, "Dondé estan?"

Her voice gave out at sundown. She went to the American café for a cup of water and drank it alone at one of the tables outside. No one had paid much attention to her that day; however, a few people had looked at her as if she was crazy. Beatriz didn't blame them. Although she didn't feel the excitement that David must have felt when he contested Goliath, asking "Dondé estan?" had made her feel better than working the diner, better than traveling all over Argentina.

That night she lay against the Pirámide wrapped in a homemade blanket, her head on her empty knapsack, rolling from side-to-side in restless sleep.

■

Day after day she rose, bought a coffee from the café, and chanted on the Pirámide. Slowly, the crowds stopped ignoring her. She didn't know if they were actually listening to what she said or if they knew why she said it, but finally, to her relief, she had a voice.

Not long afterwards, the Capital's soldiers gave her their attention. They began to pace the Plaza in small groups. Some seemed amused, some angry. One soldier was especially interested in her. She could never get a clear look at him. She often saw him watching her from the tables outside the café. When she'd go over to chant at him, to show the crowds she was unafraid of men like him, he would be gone.

■

Two weeks later, Beatriz was joined by three women. They were her age, although they looked much older. Beatriz had not seen herself in a mirror lately and thought she must look as old as them. She had not washed her hair since she left San Miguel. Her fingernails were long and dirty. She smelled of body odor. Her cotton dress was frayed. Her ragged appearance only drew more people and for that she was grateful.

As she chanted one afternoon, the three women stepped out of the crowd and onto the base of the Pirámide. Each of them had pictures of sons, daughters, and husbands. Without any prompting from Beatriz, they began chanting, "Dondé estan?"

When night fell and the crowds left, Beatriz asked them who they were. They told her their families had been taken. The pirate radio station out of Córdoba had mentioned what Beatriz was doing and they had come to see if it was true. They said at first they were afraid, but found when they chanted "Dondé estan?" they felt better than they had in years.

More mothers joined Beatriz. They came in buses, taxis, on bikes and on foot from around the country. There was Adelgonga from Patagonia and Elena from Cuyo and Diana from Posadas. There was Eva and Rayen and Paula, Martina, Elizabeth, and Natalia, all holding Rosaries and pictures of their disappeared loved ones, all burning with the desire to know, "Dondé estan?" They told Beatriz she was in the news. The pirate radio station had joined the Underground and some of its members had infiltrated the newspapers. They reported the activities of Beatriz's group, stating clearly the group's intentions, but never encouraging anyone to join. The mothers who joined Beatriz told her they did not need encouragement. The knowledge that one woman possessed such strength was enough.

When Beatriz's group began to number in the dozens, she decided they needed better organization. They began chanting in eight-hour shifts so the Capital and the Rosada heard them day and night. They made cardboard signs with enlarged pictures of their families. They talked to reporters. At the behest of Mother Luciana, they decided to make and wear white bonnets similar to Beatriz's. Beatriz could not get over the sight of the mothers, her sisters now forever, chanting in white bonnets.

The breathtaking moment for Beatriz came when the crowd at the Pirámide parted and Eva Numez walked toward her holding pictures of her daughters. Tied around her head in a makeshift bonnet was her youngest daughter's purple scarf.

■

Beatriz and the other mothers bought a full-page spread in the political section of *l'Opinion*. It showed a black-and-white grid of pictures of their disappeared loved ones. Above it, in bold print, was "Dónde están?"

Soon after the newspaper was distributed, soldiers began bothering the mothers.

One morning, a young soldier pushed his way through the crowd, some of whom booed him, and took Beatriz aside. He told her, "If you don't stop loitering at the Pirámide, we'll arrest all of you and you'll get six months in jail."

Beatriz assured him their loitering would stop. The soldier left, and Beatriz and the mothers began marching around the Plaza, moving from monument to monument.

The next day, the young solider returned and took Beatriz aside once more. He gripped her elbow and hissed, "Do you want to end up like your families?"

Beatriz laughed. "To us, what more can you do?"

■

Candles encircled the Plaza, lit by members of the Underground. They flickered as the mothers marched past them. Beatriz held her sign high, chanting, the mothers following her.

Hurrying from the back of their line, Mother Numez tugged at Beatriz's sleeve, pointing. A large man was talking with Mother Ramona and Mother Luciana on the other side of the Plaza. Beatriz squinted. She could tell he was a soldier by the stiff way he stood. "What's he want?" she asked.

Numez shrugged.

Beatriz sighed and made her way to the soldier.

Ramona and Luciana saw her coming. "He's here for you, he says," Luciana told her, pointing to the soldier. "Only you, that's what he says."

"Fine, fine," Beatriz said and pushed past Ramona.

She saw his feminine nose, his pock-marked cheeks, his hard body. His lips had thinned and there were more wrinkles around his eyes, but he was still the handsome man who'd stood at her front door and ordered her family's destruction.

The officer turned to her.

Neither of them spoke.

Finally, the officer cleared his throat and said, "Can I speak to you?"

They went in the darkness by the Capital's fence. He stood close to her.

"They want to be rid of you," the officer said.

Beatriz stood a bit straighter and said, "Try."

"I'll give you what you want," he whispered, "but only you."

"Why me?"

"Because you want to know. Because you have the right to know."

Beatriz pointed at the mothers and said, "Do they have that right, too?"

The officer shrugged. "You can decide."

■

He picked her up on Bolívar Street in a jeep with government license plates.

They drove all night. She lost track of time in the silence between them. She removed the golden money clip from her dress and gazed at the cut-out pictures of her family. She caught him looking at them and put the pictures back in the money clip and the clip back in her dress.

The high moon aided the jeep's headlights. It threw dancing, jagged shadows inside the cab. The air grew cold. Beatriz hugged herself and shivered. She figured they were heading south. Eventually, they turned off the main roads and onto dirt ones lined with thick foliage. Beatriz wanted to sleep, but wet branches kept slapping the windows, making her jump.

At dawn, they stopped at a guard post. The post was nothing more than a chain-link fence with a padlocked gate and a brick guardhouse. The lone guard, a clean-shaven boy in his late teens, lazily emerged from the guardhouse and walked toward their jeep. The officer rolled down his window. The boy saw him and his eyes widened. He stopped, stood tall, and saluted.

"Open it," the officer told him.

About a mile from the guard post the road began to crumble until it became a slender trail that snaked through heavy jungle. They drove carefully.

Beatriz caught the officer looking at her and said, "I know you."

He did not reply.

She showed him the pictures of her family.

He looked at her and said, "I don't remember."

The jungle clinging to the trail widened and gave way to a clearing atop a grassy rise. The officer parked the jeep. Through the windshield dotted with mud and grimy with dead bugs, Beatriz watched a line of black clouds roll toward them.

The officer turned off the jeep. "Get out," he said.

She fumbled with the door handle, wheezing.

The officer went to her side of the jeep and opened the door. "Get out," he repeated. She didn't move. "This is what you wanted." There was a weary bitterness in his voice.

Beatriz clenched her fists. She would not let him see her fear. She stepped out of the jeep and tried not to flinch as he slammed the door behind her.

He took her by her elbow. "This way," he muttered. He led her across the clearing, taking the rise slowly. Her body shook, her lips moved in prayer, and now, more than they had in months, her ribs pained her. She closed her eyes and gasped for breath.

They stopped.

"Open your eyes," the officer said.

She did.

Before her was a large hole. She could not see its bottom, just hundreds of tangled limbs and gaping mouths. The bodies were covered in lime, the powder thick in some places, thin in others. Men and women and boys and girls unnaturally embraced. Babies lay white and face-down, tiny fingers and toes. Stiff arms pointed at the coming storm.

The wind picked up. It began to rain. Faces became clearer, twisted, gaping. The rain revealed tattered clothing, nakedness, rot.

Beatriz looked back at the officer. She said, "You will tell the others?"

He nodded. She could not tell if there was any truth to it. "Turn around, please," he said.

Beatriz turned. Her hands found Adelmo's money clip. She held it tight. She heard the officer draw something from his belt.

She heard a metallic click.

Then, her world flickered and unspooled.

James Winter is finishing his MFA in the Northeastern Ohio Masters of Fine Arts program and currently lives in Ohio with his wife and their two mischievous cats. When not teaching rock music and movies to his students at Kent State University, he spends his time writing. His work has appeared in *The Rubbertop Review* and *Luna Negra*, where he worked as an editor.

LUMP

ELIEZRA SCHAFFZIN

Dan's lump is most easily detected in the shower under running water. He can find the tender spot with three flat fingers using a circular movement beginning at his armpit and moving along his chest. Dan's lump is on the right side and is not detectable by the naked eye. It is the size of an arcade token and slips around under his skin, evading his nervous fingertips. It is as hard as a tennis ball and hurts only when stirred by sudden movement or burdened with the weight of books or memory. On a pain scale of one to ten, where one is no pain at all and ten is the worst pain imaginable, Dan does not know where his lump belongs, since he senses he has a very capable imagination, making the scale quite vast, the numbers too far apart to be practical. The incremental fractions that separate each number, he suspects, are infinite. Oftentimes he finds he cannot imagine the scale's imaginable end. As for its humble beginnings, he worries that if he's ever experienced a scale of one, he was not sufficiently aware of this experience when it occurred. Even worse, he fears that if ever he were aware of such a thing, he might cease to exist. Dan's lump has no smell, only his skin's scent around his breast. Dan's lump is the shape of an egg and moves about as a yolk would inside its shell. Dan's lump is a powdery yellowish red like the gradual colors of a peach. Dan's lump is the size of a matchbook and feels like a wound in his side when he sleeps. Dan's lump burns sometimes, like when he's tossed and turned too much at night. It throbs at his right, pulsing opposite his heart. Dan's lump feels like a punch in his armpit when his fist pounds the air. Dan's lump is brown like the color of a river when the current stirs the mud. The River Dan overflows brown in the rain.

Dreaming, I sleep. Dan's lump leaps, lumpety-bump it is on my breast. Dan's lump sits on my breast, and spreads, in blood's deepest shade and the shape of a Victorian silhouette. Dan's lump is warm. It throbs and glows and bursts, splashing me in a hot red wave, and the liquid soaks the sheets. It slides down the windows to puddles on the floor. Out of the dark hole left behind climbs a child, wailing, tumbling onto fluid sheets. Dan's lump bursts, and it is a child on fluid red sheets, and I lift it and it is warm with tight fists and closed translucent eyelids with tiny trembling capillaries running through them every way. Underneath the lids its eyes glow yellowish-gold. Its body slips through my fingers but I gather it and hold it, squirming, between my legs. I relax and feel it settle down into silence. I push it up inside of me. I push it up, squirming again, and it is inside and I feel it rumble, warm and glowing. Then, quiet once more. Simple sloshing. I rise. We change the sheets.

Ten, Dan counts. Nine. Eight. Slowly, he thinks them through: Seven. Six. Dan lies beside me on the bed, his hair and chest still wet from the shower, smelling of soap and warmth. He holds my hand and I breathe and we wait. Five, Dan says. Four. He is counting backwards from imagination into flesh. Three. I can feel liquid turn solid, the rumbling resume. Two, Dan says. A single, expectant syllable. I sigh. Dan sighs with me, and as the air escapes his mouth shapes the word: One.

Eliezra Schaffzin, www.schaffzin.com/eliezra, is at work on a novel, a story of magic, seduction, and the early-American department store. Her short fiction and essays have appeared in or are forthcoming with *AGNI Online*, *Word Riot*, *Barrelhouse*, *Work*, and the UK-based *Sein und Werden*. She has taught writing at Harvard University and the Rhode Island School of Design.

GLOSSARY OF SELECTED TERMS
-after Nin Andrews

JONTERRI GADSON

What is: *skin*,
if not a taut swaddle

loosening; *body*
if not a warm swaddle

cooling; *blood*
if not thread

in a swaddle
made of body; *horizons*

if not lines
where the sky appears to swaddle

Earth. See *father;*
stars, if not swaddled

matter emitting light. See *spirit;*
wind if it does not trace

a swaddle's path. See *blood;*
the universe, if not the outermost circle

of concentric swaddles. See *mother;*
a *kiss*, if not mouths pressed

into twisted, wet swaddles; *taste*
if not flavor swaddling

tongue; *father*
if not the option

to swaddle; *spirit*
if not the smallest unit

of the swaddled; *mother*
if not hips

swaddling womb. See *skin*.
See *body*. See *wind*. See *universe*. See *blood*.

Jonterri Gadson is Debra's daughter. She is a Cave Canem fellow and a 2nd-year poet in the University of Virginia's Creative Writing MFA program. In the summer, she will serve as a creative writing instructor for gifted 8th–10th graders in the Duke Talent Identification Program. Her poetry has previously been published in *Muzzle*, *Torch*, *Conte*, *Poetry Quarterly*, *Diverse Voices Quarterly*, and other journals. Her poetry is forthcoming in *Sugar House Review*, and *Tidal Basin Review*.

GRAND HAVEN

ALLYSON BOGGESS

Your grandfather melts milk plastics
in the fireplace,

does it for the blue-green flame,
does it in the den,

forgets the chemtrails
that dry out our mouths

as soon as they disappear
into the ceiling.

When he leaves to buy us groceries,
I ask you to push me

onto the couch and when
you don't do it hard enough,

I ask you again and then
it is enough.

Allyson Boggess lives in Tempe, Arizona, where she teaches poetry and writing composition at Arizona State University.

CARNIVORES

JENNIFER LYNN ALESSI

Meat was scarce in the summer of 2021. The government failed to inspect some imported beef, which led to an outbreak of E. Coli. Under a botched cover-up, the bacteria spread like a blaze in a prairie, killing thousands of citizens and leading to the indiscriminate slaughter of cattle. Screening became so expensive and guarded, only the privileged few and the military had access to verified disease-free meat. The general meat ban didn't bother me—nothing did anymore—but my husband Tim was hungry for it.

Three months into the ban, our new neighbors arrived: Joe and Shirley Grazio, an army sergeant and his young wife. They brought few possessions, and their furniture seemed to consist of card tables and folding chairs. They apparently moved around a lot, and with the husband's hand in a cast and the wife very pregnant, it made sense not to lug things around. There was nothing that immediately aroused our suspicions; and even if there were, I doubt we would have bothered investigating: I just wanted to be left alone, and one thing they did bring was meat.

Shortly after they moved in, our neighbors began inviting us for cookouts, and with one look at Tim's face I couldn't refuse. While the men hovered by the grill, I lay on a chaise wearing sunglasses and the red beach cover-up that had become my outdoor robe, my stiffened pose trying to ward Shirley, seated beside me, away. At another time, we might have been two amiable couples in suburban Baltimore on a Sunday afternoon, grilling meat on their shared patch of grass, in front of matching sliding-glass doors. But the oil wars had taken their toll, as had the spike in gas, the loss of jobs and lack of meat. Even the newscasters openly displayed an air of exasperation. Nearly everyone, it seemed, lived for the moment each day when they could start anesthetizing themselves from the wreck of the world with cheap liquor. But not Shirley; it seemed she longed for human *connection*, and that required an energy and felicity I no longer had.

While she was needy, her husband was insufferable. "What would you have grilled?" he kept asking my husband.

"Grilled cheese?" Tim said, then winked at me. He was a man who perpetually found a bright side, who desired agreeableness above all else.

Fork in his good hand, Joe pierced a steak. "You're lucky we're neighbors," he added, nodding to both Tim then me. Several emptied beer cans lay on the grass by his feet. Though eight months pregnant, Shirley had been collecting them in a trash bag to hide how much he drank until Joe had shot her a look. He flipped the meat onto its raw side, and it fell off the grill.

"Oh!" Shirley gasped as if it had burned her.

"It's fine," Tim assured us. He picked the steak off the grass and, buzzed himself, wiped it on the thigh of his jeans. "Beth will eat it, won't you?"

"Absolutely," I replied.

He crouched beside my chaise, tore off a piece and fed it to me.

I licked his fingers, and Shirley blushed.

She stared down at the magazine in her lap. "Fresh-squeezed juice may harm a baby," she read. "It can contain bacteria their developing stomachs can't digest." Then she marveled, "Is nothing *safe*?"

"Not a thing," I answered, casually, "not anymore."

Tim glanced at her swollen belly then sadly shook his head at me. I'd disappointed him, as I had a lot lately. And if only to stop disappointing him, I wished I could be kind.

With a nervous smile, Shirley closed the magazine. She was a small bony woman in a straw hat whose skin burned easily.

"Don't tell me how unsafe the world is," Joe interjected. "I was shot, you know."

We knew. He'd told us the story a half dozen times.

"While protecting your mother, right?" Tim asked, to my chagrin.

"Joe?" Shirley said. "Sweetheart. You already told them."

"So?" Joe grumbled. "It's a hero's story."

He told it again, and I barely listened. It was a story too self-righteous to believe: he was visiting his elderly mother in Baltimore, in an Italian neighborhood where she'd lived for forty years. Despite his urging, she'd refused to move or let him hire an aide for protection, though the *gang bangers*—his words—were encroaching from all sides. While she slept, he sat by her bed, holding her hand. He fell asleep then woke to the sound of smashing glass, a dark face in the window, and the glare of a flashlight beam. Joe held up his hand to the light as he stormed toward the glass. Startled, the would-be robber shot him through the palm before fleeing. The bullet shattered Joe's hand and nicked his lung. It was a pain, he stressed, that was beyond our imaginations.

When it started to rain, I hoped our cookout would come to an early end. But Tim extended the awning above

Shirley and me before helping Joe move the grill. Through the feeble patter, I could hear Joe lecturing my husband—an independent contractor—about the danger of rust.

Nine months ago I would have been busy, correcting papers for the composition classes I taught at a local community college. I'd cover the students' essays with comments aimed at fostering their rhetorical skills and critical thinking. I *believed* in them, in my power to help them, to change this world for the better, in whatever small way I could. And they believed in me. But even before most of the funding for higher ed. was cut, it seemed this world was bent on sucking that faith from all of us.

I lay back in the chaise, closing my eyes, feeling the beer I'd drunk and the tremendous heat. Even the rain slanting under the tarp was warm on my face. Though I tried to shut her out, I could hear Shirley breathing beside me, could sense her hands clasped protectively over her womb.

"Beth?" she said.

I pretended not to hear.

She leaned toward me, her short hair falling away from her neck. I could feel the strands, almost, brushing my skin. "Beth," she whispered, "Joe almost died."

"I know."

"The bullet hit his lung. It wouldn't have been so frightening if the bullet hadn't hit his lung."

"He seems fine now," I told her.

"Oh, no, Beth, he's not," she sobbed. Then she reached her pale, bony hand toward mine.

■

We couldn't afford to run the air conditioner at night, so Tim and I slept naked on top of the sheets. He'd rigged the fan so its cord fell over the headboard, and with one small tug the blades moved the air. We'd only pull it after sex. Only recently I'd found the keys to mindlessness: rough sex while drunk in a hot, dark room.

For the first nine years of our marriage, we'd agreed not to have children. With overpopulation and the starvation of millions around the world, we couldn't justify bringing a new life into it. But two years ago my mother died of stomach cancer, and though her passing wasn't unexpected it still sent me into a tailspin. The only thought that seemed to right me, and Tim by association, was having a baby. I went off the pill and we became that insular couple I'd always disdained—our lives revolving around ovulation charts, Tim carving a cradle to help the universe along. It didn't take too long. Within six months, I was pregnant. I wore maternity clothes to school long before it was necessary; and when it was, I happily waddled down the halls. When I was laid off weeks before my scheduled leave, I learned to knit and created a cubby full of sweaters. At Tim's suggestion, because CNN got me too worked up, I began to watch baking shows instead of news reports. When we learned our baby was a girl, we debated names into the night, each one forming a different perfect child in our heads. Each afternoon I took long ambling walks, delighting in our baby's kicks while marveling at the nature that was somehow left unblemished around us.

Occasionally, on instinct, I'd turn on the news. And at the report of the latest workplace rampage or escalated level-of-terror, I'd feel a surge of heartburn and quickly shut it off. Still, every day or two, I'd turn it on again. Then, four weeks before my due date, at a normal check-up, the doctor detected irregularities in my baby's heartbeat. I was rushed in for an emergency C-section. Legs clamped in stirrups, arms held by nurses, I craned to see over the sheet the doctor insisted hang between me and my womb. There was a flutter of attendees, smocks smeared with blood, a din of equipment then an unspeakable silence. I looked into Tim's eyes, and when I saw the anguish there I couldn't look anywhere else. Despite his assurances, I knew I was to blame for being too hideously weak to protect our baby from the world.

And now, back on the pill, I rubbed my face against his. He rolled on top of me and entered without foreplay. I scratched his back, and knew I was leaving marks.

■

At five each morning, Tim took the keys off the bureau and drove to Baltimore. He was remodeling a townhouse for a corporate client, which was all he seemed to have these days. I slept late each morning because I could.

At eleven, Shirley would drag a card table onto the patio and set up the portable TV for Joe to watch. He liked cop shows and he liked them loud. "Bad boys, Bad boys"—I'd wake to the thumping theme song and a shower of bullets. Then in my indoor robe, sipping coffee and reading Dickens on the couch, I'd see the shapes their bodies projected and couldn't help glimpsing them through the blinds: Shirley pouring him a drink from the decanter, Joe stroking the cast on his hand.

Once her husband was engrossed in the show, Shirley would hover before my slider like a bird attempting to gauge if the window were air or glass. Then one day she went ahead, raised her hand and knocked.

I put down my book and opened the door. "Yes?"

"Can you come over for coffee?" she asked in a rush.

"Thanks," I told her. "But I'm reading."

"Danielle Steele?"

"Not Danielle Steele."

Her smooth brow crinkled. "What's wrong with Danielle Steele?"

"Nothing's wrong with her."

She stared down at her sandals. "Are you mad at me, Beth?"

"Of course not."

"Please," she whispered. "I have no one else."

Without bothering to change, I went out. If I didn't and Tim somehow learned of her desperate plea, it would be more evidence of callousness that might ultimately drive him away. I followed her past the card table to her slider door, but as she drew it open, Joe turned away from the screen.

"Where do you think you're going?" he demanded.

"Inside, for coffee." She was actually wringing her hands.

"Coffee?" he scoffed. "You don't drink coffee, and I guarantee that Beth prefers bourbon."

"Indeed," I said.

While Shirley blushed from ear to ear, I sat down at the table and helped myself to Joe's liquor.

"Unbelievable!" he exclaimed, motioning to the TV. "They all run around, blasting their guns, acting like it's no big deal."

"It *is* a cop show," I pointed out.

He looked at me. "Have you ever felt a bullet, Beth?"

"Literally or figuratively?"

"Sweetheart," he said. "There's only one kind."

I emptied my glass then pretended to have an upset stomach. As I headed to my slider, I could hear Joe behind me, remarking to Shirley, "Told you, she's a lightweight, that one."

■

When Tim came home that afternoon, I met him at the front door. Without letting him get settled, I blurted out what had been on my mind since the morning: "I think Joe arranged to get himself shot."

"Seriously?" He laughed, kicking off his boots. "Why would he do that?"

"To avoid being redeployed, to collect disability while still enjoying the meat. These incidents are not uncommon, Tim."

"You watch too much news," he said.

He headed to the kitchen, and I followed close behind.

"It makes sense," I continued, knowingly disappointing him with each word but unable to stop. "Think of the way they act. Joe's such a goddamn brute and Shirley's always tiptoeing around him. It's like she's realized what he's done and is afraid of what he's capable of. And that story about his comatose mother and the random intruder. It's too convenient to believe."

"Just stay out of it, Beth."

"I want to, believe me. But Shirley keeps dragging me in. She invited me over for coffee this morning and acted so desperate about it. It's like she wanted to confide something, like it's eating her up inside."

He opened the fridge, took out two beers and handed one to me. "Come on," he groaned. "You're imagining things. Let it go."

And I tried.

But later, he smelled hickory and smoke. They were barbecuing, ribs this time. I had boiled six eggs and lumped in mayonnaise for dinner, but had forgotten to buy bread in my online order. We took our beers out to the patio.

Shirley smiled as she finished setting the table, but her hands shook as she laid down each dish. "There's plenty to go around," she offered.

"That is, if you're not still sick, Beth," Joe added.

"Sick?" Tim asked, glancing at me.

"It was just my period," I told them.

I assumed my prone position on the chaise, and Shirley sat in a folding chair beside me. She was wearing a frilly yellow short set that would have been more appropriate on a four-year-old. Her cheeks and chest were sunburned. Her legs were spread apart, the knees red, thighs white. She patted her stomach. "Want to feel?" she asked, with the same grating need.

"No."

Her eyes grew wide, then she laughed. "You're not squeamish, are you?"

"Not at all."

"You're squeamish, Beth!" she cried.

"Squeamish?" Joe remarked. "Then have I got something to show you." He pulled up his t-shirt and turned around. There was a large, puckered scar to the left of his spine. "Exit wound," he said.

"Honey," Shirley pleaded.

"I'm just getting started, Shirl."

She gave a tight smile. "They don't want to see that, Joe."

"Yes, I do," I said. I walked over to Joe, lifted my hand to it and felt the crushed skin. I glanced at my husband. Eyes focused on the grill, he was turning the ribs though they were already done.

■

That night, Tim and I lay in bed without speaking. The heat and the silence were overwhelming. "Joe arranged his own shooting," I announced into the darkness. "And now he's got the nerve to parade the scar."

Tim reached for the cord and turned on the fan. Its blades whirred in the air above us. "We should tell them about Lauren," he stated.

"Absolutely not."

"They think we don't like them."

"We don't."

"They think that we're cruel."

"I am cruel, Tim."

"Oh, no," he said. "No, Beth." Then he touched me, too carefully.

■

He fell asleep and I stayed awake, smoking cigarettes in my robe on the patio. I'd quit during pregnancy, then promptly started up again. I hid them from Tim and smoked until I could feel my lungs. Sometime later, I heard the squeak of a slider and turned to see Shirley in a white nightgown, stepping out to join me. I grabbed my cigarettes and started to head inside, but as she drew closer I could see she was crying.

"Oh, Beth," she whispered, sinking into the chair beside me. "Thank god you're here. I have no one to talk to. My parents are out west. I met Joe when he was stationed in San Diego. I'm not sure if you knew that." She paused to wipe her runny nose with her hand. "I want to talk to them so badly, but I'm afraid of the phone."

I lit another cigarette, blew the smoke away from her and tried not to sound interested. "You're afraid of the phone?"

She nodded. "That Joe will hear me. That they'll overhear me."

"Who's they?"

She looked at me, chin trembling, then lowered her voice even more. "I have to trust you."

It wasn't a question.

"Joe's under investigation. And the military could be tapping our phone."

"It's the shooting, isn't it?"

Her jaw dropped.

I softened my tone, pleased that I'd been right. "You don't have to be a detective to figure it out."

"You know," she said, excitedly, as fresh tears began to well in her eyes. "You *understand.* Joe thought I was crazy and made me promise not to tell you. But you're a woman; I knew you'd understand! You'd know he couldn't go back there when so many of his men never made it home alive. He was just thinking of me and our baby."

"It was his decision," I told her. "You're not to blame."

Joe, on the other hand, was culpable in my eyes, not for his crime primarily, but for his gall. And Shirley, it occurred to me then as something like tenderness rose beneath my ribs, might be one of the few innocent adults left in this world.

"You don't hate me then?" she asked. "You don't think that I'm awful?"

"Why would I?"

"You don't know how much that means to me, Beth!"

"I'm glad."

"I've been replaying that night over and over in my mind. If I'd just held my hand steady, everything would have been all right. But I panicked, and when the police came I bungled the whole story. Joe's furious, of course, and the idea of being disgraced is tearing him up inside. He's become so angry, I'm even scared of him sometimes, but I know in my heart that's not the real Joe. He insisted on moving us here to a more affordable condo. And if they come for him, he insists on keeping me out of it and taking all the blame. But how can I live with myself when everything's my fault?"

She was leaning forward, and her hand had come to rest on my knee. She was kneading it as she spoke. My cigarette, between my fingers, had since gone out. When she was finished, she raised her pleading eyes to mine, and all I felt was a lump in my throat.

As if noticing my shift, Shirley withdrew her hand. Meekly she lamented, "I don't know what to do. Any second they could take my Joey away. Our baby's coming in two weeks and I don't know what to do."

"Neither do I," I said, as nicely as I could.

■

The next day, Tim came home early. He rushed into the living room, sawdust still flecking his skin. "Are you okay?" he asked.

"I'm fine, honey." I was at the computer, proofreading the affidavit I'd spent the night writing after researching the proper format and language. The process had brought a renewed satisfaction of pouring myself into something and getting it right.

"Then why did you sleep out here?"

I kissed his lips then went to the kitchen, fixed us two rum punches and asked him to join me on the couch. I relayed everything Shirley had told me, and everything I was now determined to do.

He held my hand throughout the story. And when I was done, he stared down at his fingers laced with mine, looking more concerned than if I'd slept on the lawn. "No," he said. "We're not going to do anything."

I pulled my hand away. "Why the hell not?"

"What good would it do?"

"We'd be reporting a crime!"

"The world's a crime! These wars are crimes. How is ruining their lives going to help this world one bit?"

"But he's so arrogant."

"He was protecting his family."

"He's so self-righteous."

"He was protecting his child."

I'd become hysterical but couldn't make myself calm down. "And Shirley—she acts so innocent, so *helpless*, but she's guilty as well."

"For God's sake!" he shouted, standing up and heading to the door. "Who's innocent and who hasn't suffered? But not everyone shuts themselves off from the world, Beth. Not everyone has to grieve in the exact same way as you."

■

A short time later, through the wall we could hear Joe shouting at Shirley: "You told her! You *fucking* told her!" Then Shirley's response, as desperate as a mantra, "Joe, they're our friends."

Holding me at arm's length, Tim looked me in the eyes. "Here's what we're going to do," he said. "We're going to invite them over for dinner. We're going to smooth this all over."

And I was too afraid to refuse.

■

He went out and bought more rum and ice for the blender. From a market by the harbor, he picked up fresh lobsters and salmon in case Shirley didn't eat shellfish while pregnant. For the first time in months, it seemed, I changed out of my robe. I showered and put on a red sundress with spaghetti straps—Tim's favorite—then assumed the role of dutiful hostess. I cleaned up the condo, set the table and put out snacks. I did it all without hesitation until I saw our neighbors outside, approaching the slider.

Shirley was clutching Joe's arm with one hand and balancing a pie on the other. Joe was staring at me through the glass with unmitigated rage.

Luckily, Tim saw them too and rushed past me to let them in.

Smiling, he shook Joe's hand then took the pie from Shirley. "Thanks. Wow, you look great," he told her, though she clearly didn't. Her coral pink maternity dress made her skin look blotchier than ever, and her eyes were so red-rimmed and swollen I suspected she'd cried all day.

"Cut the crap," Joe grumbled. He extracted himself from Shirley's grip and dropped down on the couch.

"Will you excuse me?" I said, then dashed to the kitchen and stood by the sink, pretending to watch a pot.

"Joe's just tired," I heard Shirley explaining in a rush. "Aren't you, honey?"

"Tired, Shirl? You could say that."

"Drinks, anyone?" Tim asked then joined me in the kitchen. "Please, for me," he whispered and nipped at my ear.

"Beer?" I called to them. "Pina Coladas?"

"The stronger the better," Joe answered.

I crushed the ice with a mallet then poured a pint of rum into the blender, hoping to knock us all out.

"We've got salmon, Shirley," Tim called to her, while arranging crackers in a neat swirl on a plate, "in case you don't eat shellfish."

"I love salmon," Shirley gushed.

"Since when?" Joe snapped.

Then I heard her say, softly, "Joe."

"What, Shirl? We can't be honest? They're our friends, right?"

I brought the drinks into the living room on a silver tray held high and pretended they were customers. I was their waitress, and soon they would leave.

"Here you are," I said, unthinkingly handing a Pina Colada to Shirley.

"Oh, no," she gasped, her hands on her stomach.

"Some friend," Joe said, and I set both drinks before him.

"We've decided what to name our baby," Shirley anxiously piped in. "I know it's old-fashioned not to find out the sex beforehand, but we wanted a nice surprise. If it's a boy, we'll name him Joe Junior. If it's a girl, Elizabeth."

"Not after you," Joe added, sucking down his drink. "My mother's name is Elizabeth."

"What a lovely coincidence," I told him.

"Isn't it?"

"I can't take this anymore!" Shirley cried. "Beth. Joe knows about last night. But what he doesn't know is that you wouldn't do anything to hurt us."

"That's right," Tim assured them, coming into the living room with a plate of cubed cheese. "We're friends."

■

The four of us sat at the dark-wood table, eyes focused on our own plates. Tim, Joe and I dug into our lobsters, cracking open the legs and claws, while Shirley ran her fork over her salmon, lifting flakes of pink meat. "I'm a little scared," she said, responding to a question that no one had asked. "Of the pain, I mean. I just want to be conscious while it's happening."

"Unconscious is better," I said.

"It's funny," she continued, seemingly lost in her own world. "I've always known it was supposed to hurt, but I never really thought about the pain until now. Imagine that. A baby fitting through there."

"Shirl," Joe broke in, and his words were thick. "It can't be that bad. Millions of women for millions of years have given birth."

"But I'm me."

"That's right, honey." Joe patted her arm. "You're you."

"And I'm afraid." She slid her chair back from the table. "I'm sorry. It's just the hormones talking." She dabbed at her eyes with a napkin, then abruptly stood and rushed out the slider door.

Tim touched my thigh. "Go after her," he said.

And I did.

I found her in the complex's rundown playground, sitting on a swing. It was dusk and there were no children around. Except for Shirley—she'd never seemed more like a child to me than at that moment—her hands wrapped around the rusted chains, her head lowered, toes dragging in the dirt.

I stopped before her, and she gazed up.

"Oh, Beth," she sobbed, wiping her nose with the back of her hand. "I'm so sorry I ruined dinner."

I stood with my arms crossed over my chest. "Why don't you come back then?"

She shook her head and stared at the ground. I thought of the lobster on my plate, of scraping the meat from the tail. Then suddenly, Shirley's chest and back convulsed in a wracking sob. "Oh please, God, help me," she wailed, and in that desolate playground I felt as if there were no God at all. "Please, God, forgive me," she groaned, lifting a face distorted with tears.

I began to turn away from her, from the weight of her, but she rushed up and flung her body against mine. She clasped her arms around my neck and pressed her cheek against my face.

"*Please*," she begged, in a pitch that made my chest rise, in a wretched depth I recognized as my own species' animal cry of despair. "I'm so scared! Don't leave me all alone in this! Don't tell me I'm all alone."

I swallowed, and felt my own tears rising like a hot spring in a desert, like a finally welcome release. I thought of telling her how much I missed my mother, how terrified I was of trying for a baby again, how tenuous my marriage had become and how hideous I felt. But instinctively I knew there would be plenty of time for that. For now, I stroked her hair with my hand then cupped it gently over her skull.

"It's okay," I soothed. "We'll be all right," I told her, and to my ears it was a lie. But then, she held me tighter, and suddenly it wasn't.

Jennifer Lynn Alessi holds a BA in English from Columbia University and an MFA in Creative Writing from the University of Alaska Anchorage. Her work has appeared in *Parnassus*, *Passages North*, *Quarterly West*, and other journals. Recently, she completed a first novel—an upmarket women's fiction inspired by a year on the road with a traveling circus.

PREGNANT ON THE EL TRAIN

CHRISTOPHER NEWGENT

When you got on at Pulaski, I stood and offered you my seat. I didn't even hesitate. You looked tired, slack-shouldered and cradling your belly.

I'm always amazed how you as a woman can build bones inside your body. I worry about your bones, you have such small wrists. I read once how some women crave gravel, how some deep part of their bodies knows of the stone's iron and calcium, a woman who kept a limestone pebble in her mouth the last 4 months of pregnancy.

In a dream last night, I saw you in your driveway on hands and knees, shoveling scoop by scoop into your mouth. I wanted to go to you, offer you a glass of milk, but you had swallowed up all the earth between us. In the canyon below a museum of fossils, and you gnawing and gnawing.

Christopher Newgent lives in Indianapolis where he runs Vouched Books and the Vouched Presents reading series to promote small press literature in his community. You can find more about this at vouchedbooks. com, or see more of his work at cenewgent.com.

HOMOSEXUALS THREATEN THE SANCTITY OF NORMAN'S MARRIAGE

JOHN WARNER

They started in on a Tuesday, late Fall. It was morning, and as Norman took the garbage to the curb, he could see them loosely huddled near the bagged leaves that waited for pickup. Dammit, he thought. Homosexuals in the yard.

They'd come to threaten the sanctity of his marriage, but Norman wasn't having it.

"Morning," he said. Norman tries to be friendly to everybody regardless. That's how he was raised. American values.

"Good morning," they replied. A couple of them wore nicely tailored suits that looked just a bit snug in the seat. One of them had a lime green sweater tied around his neck. Their grooming was impeccable. Another had a perfectly straight trail of hair plunging down his chest, accentuated by the open front of his shirt. Still another was clad entirely in leather. He squeaked whenever he moved. A few of them looked just about like anyone else. To Norman, they all smelled citrusy. Norman turned to make his way back to the house.

"You don't show her the proper attention," one of them called after him.

"Excuse me?" Norman replied.

"Your wife, you take her for granted," another said.

"I love my wife."

They looked at each other and smiled. "Of course you do." The man with the lime green sweater slipped his arm around the waist of one that looked just about like anyone else. "But when's the last time you *really* looked at her," he said. The other man turned to face the man with the sweater. They closed their eyes and brought their faces close together, brushing their noses.

Norman didn't need to see that stuff. He went back inside.

Ellie was moving around the kitchen. Those fellows didn't know what they were talking about. Norman looked at his wife every day. Norman watched as she took the breakfast plates from the table to the sink. Her bottom shook underneath her robe as she scrubbed the plates. Her hair medium length and brown. The ankles thicker than you'd think, but not in a bad way. Norman had been looking at her for years. How many years? Thirty-six years. What was left to see?

Norman stood to leave for work. He wondered if he should say something to Ellie about the homosexuals outside, or if it would just cause her worry. Ellie placed the dishes in the washer. Norman cleared his throat as if to speak and Ellie turned to look at him and smiled, waving the scrub brush in farewell. Saying nothing, Norman walked out of the kitchen, to the garage, to the car. He backed out of the garage and driveway without looking, wondering if he might feel a bump as he ran over the whole pack of them.

■

Norman didn't see them for awhile after that first encounter, but then one evening, as he went to retrieve the recycling bin, there they were, playing hopscotch along the sidewalk. There seemed to be more of them this time. They clapped loudly for each other as they went for each successive square. Norman thought it, but didn't say it, *fairies.*

"We've been meaning to tell you," the one with the lime green sweater said, dribbling his stone into a hopscotch square, "your moves in the bedroom, they're limited."

"What do you mean?"

"For one thing, are you always on top?" he asked, hopping towards his stone.

"Is there another way?"

"Would you like us to demonstrate?" he paused and looked at Norman.

"Lord no," he said.

"We could show you some things…" the one in the lime green sweater held his hands outstretched at his waist and pumped his hips forward.

"No, please, no."

"Homophobic?"

"Midwestern."

They laughed. Norman did a little as well. He knew deep down he wasn't homophobic. He was pretty positive he'd known some gays, treated them well, treated them just like anyone else. He didn't hate anyone for what they were or for what they chose to be. That just wasn't Norman's way.

The one with the lime green sweater tied around his neck stood on one foot and bent to retrieve his stone, his arm stretched down, his leg levering into the air from his hip.

"Anytime, though, if you want," he said, skipping back to safety.

Not always on top. Mostly, but not every time, Norman thought. Ellie had been his only and his always, and that should mean something. They were getting older for sure, but they were not dormant, no sirs. Some nights, they would be watching television side by side on the couch and their knees touch and there would be a little twitch up Norman's leg, an ache that climbs to you know where, and it is the same ache as when she first let him kiss her under the bleachers, back in high school, when they went outside to steal a smoke, and Norman leaned into her, as though drawn by a magnet, pressing his lips harder against hers until she ducked away and he clanged his head against one of the support bars.

So those nights, once in bed, Norman will slide her nightgown up and run the back of his nail along her thigh, and that is his sign and hers is a change in her breathing, deeper, longer, and when she is ready, she will slip out from underneath her nightgown and Norman will shed his bottoms and climb on top of her, bracing himself on his elbows so as not to crush her, and there they are. One man and one woman, together. As it was in the Garden, as it has been since, and as it should be forever.

■

They were back again, a few weeks later. It had snowed and Norman was out shoveling the drive. They wore puffy winter coats with fur-trimmed hoods, except for the leather-clad one who still wore his leather, now accentuated with matching gloves, and the average ones who wore long overcoats. As Norman cleared the snow, they frolicked in the yard, making snow angels and flinging snowballs at each other. Frankly, Norman thought, they threw like girls.

The one with the lime green sweater ran up towards Norman, clutching a fistful of snow, cocking his arm back.

"Please don't," he said.

He dropped the snow to the ground and brushed his hands together. "I wouldn't," he said. Norman scraped another strip of the drive clean, piled the snow into berms along the sides.

"So," he said.

"What?"

"Gina," he said. He stretched the name out (Geeee-nahhh) and smiled and looked up at Norman out from under his hood. He wiggled his eyebrows.

"What does that mean?"

"Gina," he said, "from work. You watch her. She *is* hot. Even we can see that. We may be gay, but we're not dead."

Gina. She had some skirts, no doubt about it, Norman was not dead either. Her mode of dress was not really appropriate for the workplace, but Norman had not made a careful study of her wardrobe or anything. He'd always been a faithful man to Ellie and ogling women was rude. "I don't know what you're talking about," he said.

"Hawwwww," he laughed, tilting his head back. "That wasn't your wife you were thinking about bending over the copier and tugging her panties down as your trousers dropped to your ankles. I'm pretty sure of that one."

 So this was their game, Norman thought, sow doubt, undermine traditions with their free love hedonism. He wasn't going to have any of it. He'd thought no such things. Norman raised the shovel over his head, "back off!"

"Whoa, big guy," he said, raising his hands and retreating. "Don't kill the messenger, my man. We're not here to harm." He turned and jogged back to his companions and rejoined the hijinks. Norman quickly finished the driveway and retreated inside.

■

Gina. Was it possible that she began to linger overly long at Norman's desk? She is younger than him, but not so much younger. Twelve years? Fifteen? Twenty? She is lean and her walk is strong. She smiles at him often, but then Norman is her boss and this is not a bad strategy with a boss. Norman knows this that the gender dynamics have changed over the years and that successful women sometimes use their womanness to their advantage. Her skirts stretch very tightly over her hips and they ride up high. Norman does not remember this style of skirt on the young women of his generation. In high school, the boys would duck their heads to peek at the girls' calves beneath their hemlines, and that's what he first saw of Ellie. The ankles, a bit thick, yes, but the calves, shapely, promising something interesting higher on the leg. The skirts now, there is no imagining necessary, though seeing them, the imagination races, Norman thinks, and not in a good way. And the breasts, they tremble above the open neck of her blouse, a small charm tumbles down the gap from a necklace, inviting one to look. The cold winter days, she entered the office, hugged in a heavy coat, covered, but then she shook free from the coat and there she was, all of her, the skirt, the blouse.

These newer styles seemed wrong, inappropriate, but…effective…was the word that came to Norman's mind.

■

They started showing up at work, one or two of them in the bathroom or the kitchenette. Norman wondered how they got past security. Everyone in the building was supposed to wear a name badge. "So," the one with the lime green sweater said, "dinner with Gina."

"It's with the whole team," Norman replied, stirring powdered creamer into his coffee. "Thanks for a job well done."

The man frowned down at Norman's cup. "How do you drink that crap?" he said. "Ever hear of a mochaccino?"

"I've been drinking it every day, and no, I wouldn't know about mochaccinos."

The man went to the fridge and pawed through the leftover lunches, grimacing at the Chinese take-out containers and a half eaten Caesar salad with breaded chicken strips. "Ugh, you people are going to eat yourselves into your graves. Want to see my six-pack?"

"Is there something you wanted," Norman said, sighing.

He shut the fridge and turned to Norman. "You drink that sludge every day, and I'm sure you think it suits you just fine, but the truth is, I've seen you drive by the coffee places and you're curious about the lattes, the mochaccinos, the frappaccinos."

"I don't even know what those are, nor do I care," Norman said. Though truthfully, Norman often found himself staring at the windows of these coffee places that suddenly seemed everywhere, wondering about the possibilities inside, but he would never go in for fear of making himself the fool by ordering wrongly. "Why break what doesn't need fixing?" Norman said.

Norman thought the man looked at him with something like pity, but it should've been the other way around given his situation, his status. "If you say so," the man said, flouncing out of the kitchenette and into the hallway.

■

"I won't be home tomorrow night," Norman said to Ellie, as they sat down to dinner that evening. Wednesday, which meant meatloaf, which Norman enjoyed with generous mounds of ketchup.

"No?"

"I'm taking the whole team out to celebrate. We're up 22% this year over last." Norman shook the ketchup bottle vigorously, mixing the contents, making sure he wasn't stuck with a runny initial burst out of the squeeze top.

"No spouses?"

"They're all single, dearest. Besides, it isn't in the budget."

"Even though you're up 22%?"

Norman could not tell whether or not Ellie was teasing him. Her face was bent over her plate as she shoveled a forkful of green beans into her mouth.

Norman got a little huffy, "We're the only ones up more than single digits. Some groups are even down." He crammed a bite of meatloaf into his mouth and chewed roughly. Looking up, he could see two or three of the homosexuals outside the window over Ellie's shoulder, waving at him like little children. Norman frowned.

"That's wonderful, dear," Ellie said. "I just wish I could be in on the celebration is all. I'm proud of you." Her voice trailed off near the end, becoming barely audible, but this didn't matter because he was distracted by the antics of the homosexuals. One of the suit wearing ones donned a long dark wig and hung a sign around his neck with "Gina" written on it in bold letters. The lime green sweatered one came up from behind and groped the other man's chest while thrusting his pelvis against his backside. Norman tried to wave them off without Ellie seeing, but as she looked up, she caught him flailing his arms back and forth.

"Are you okay?" she said.

"Fine," Norman replied, digging his fork back into the meatloaf. "Maybe a little dry tonight."

"Maybe," Ellie said. "The beef looked a bit old in the case."

■

The plan—never stated, but understood between them—had been for children, somewhere between several and a bunch. They weren't exactly trying from the get-go, but neither were they using any protection. At first, they rationalized, Norman was moving up the ladder and when children did arrive they'd have increased security and stability, God would grant them their blessings when they were ready to receive them. After awhile, it seemed strange, though, all that activity with nothing (not nothing, but you know…) to show for it. Norman first turned to God, praying for it, not for his sake, but Ellie's. When that didn't work, and they felt the window of opportunity closing, they went to the doctor, a humiliation.

They handed Norman a cup with a screw-top lid, his name and a six digit number written on the side and showed him to a room with a reclining chair, a couch and an array of skin magazines in a rack on the wall. It wasn't that Norman never masturbated, but he certainly didn't make a habit of it and did his best to think of Ellie when he did so. The magazines looked old, the pages worn. The women seemed eager to show the viewer their privates, making sure everything was spread for examination. They were nearly shaved completely. Norman realized he had never seen Ellie *down there*. He'd felt it, of course, and once or twice – more out of duty than desire – used his mouth, but it was always dark when they made love and when he tried it, Ellie would pull his head away and he would mount.

The pictures did nothing for Norman except make him shudder, but as he closed his eyes and tried to conjure Ellie, she stayed fuzzy and out of reach, and so he reached for one of the magazines and turned to a picture where the woman had one arm slung under her breasts, pushing them up and together, while her fingers reached for her privates. Norman covered her lower half with his free hand and made his deposit, the spunk sad and gray under the overhead fluorescents. When he was done, not knowing why, he carefully tore the page from the magazine and folded it until it fit into a slot in his wallet.

The doctors said that individually there was nothing wrong with Norman and Ellie, but a fluke of body chemistry made his sperm incompatible with her womb. Ellie reached for Norman's hand and began to cry when they received the news. Norman gripped it back and nodded stoically. The doctors said that when Norman's swimmers entered Ellie they became disoriented, like they were drunk, and swam the wrong direction or in circles. It is the kind of thing they rarely see, the doctor said, but they do see it from time to time. Some remedies were being tried for this condition, but as of yet, nothing had proven promising. Still, conception was not impossible. Some of the sperm seemed to get the gist, just not enough to make the odds good ones. The doctor smiled at them and said, "The only thing to do is just keep trying, and have fun doing it!"

They were counseled on in vitro fertilization, but when they were told what happens to the leftover embryos, that was the end of that. You can't kill ten babies to make one and feel good about that.

But for a while they did not try, Ellie turning her back to Norman as she slid under the sheets, a cool wall of air separating them in the bed. In the middle of the night Norman would wake with an erection and clenched fists. After several months, Ellie began throwing a leg over his body as they slept, and finally, one early morning, just before dawn he felt Ellie's hand groping at his legs and they were together again. They tried and tried, less often but regularly and there were a few what they dubbed close calls, but were just late periods, nothing close at all. One day they realized they'd both crossed forty and the odds had gone from negligible to non-existent and that even adoption, at least of an infant was a long shot. Norman did his best to count his blessings received, health, a wife whom he loved and who loved him, success in business. To complain seemed ungracious, and yet he often thought about how unfair it seemed. Deep down he knew he had what it took to be a good father: the capacity for love, a willingness to sacrifice, a deep sense of ethics and morality, the instinct to protect combined with an openness to letting go when the time is right. Norman knew that fatherhood would be *fulfilling*, the endpoint of his destiny, and he was pretty sure that Ellie felt the same about motherhood.

After it became apparent that their lives together would be childless, without saying a word to each other they stopped trying. This is not to say that they never made love – they were human beings with needs – but each year

Norman felt more and more of the need leaking out of him. Even so, his love for Ellie did not diminish, even as his desire was slowly extinguished.

He shouldn't have had so much to drink. Normally he limited himself to one glass of wine, two at the most if the dinner was going to be a prolonged one. They had been drinking cocktails that ended in "tini" and looked radioactive in the glass and Norman had lost count at six. He knew he was talking too loud and too much, regaling the team – Bart, Laurie, Sheila, Ian, Scarlet, and of course, Gina – with ancient tales from the company offices. He spilled secrets, some of which weren't his to give away and after each story, he saw them look at each other as if to say, "get a load of this," before goading him on. He felt like a racehorse being spurred by the jockey. It was a large table and he sat at the head with Gina on his right and underneath the table at some point she'd put her hand on his knee, but he didn't miss a beat. When the waiter came to clear the dinner plates, Norman had hardly eaten any of his steak and pommes frites, but he sent the plate away anyway and launched back into another story. It felt like he'd been waiting his whole life to be in this place, with these people, *his* people, hanging on his experiences, his wisdom. Bart suggested an aperitif and when Norman stood to retire to the bar the room swirled and he clutched the table and he felt Gina reach for his elbow, keeping him steady.

It was as though leaving the table broke the spell and in the bar, the others picked up the conversation, airing typical workplace complaints about non-understanding bosses and stupid managerial moves. Norman was rooted to a stool, afraid that if he tried to stand he would sway in place. While he cringed a little at the criticism rained down on his longtime friends and colleagues, Norman felt flattered that they would air these grievances in front of him, making it clear that he, Norman, was one of the good guys. He tried his best to nod or smile at the right spots without seeming too eager. One by one everyone else excused themselves for the evening, until Norman was alone with Gina and she came up to his stool and put her knee between his legs.

"I guess I'm just not tired yet, are you?" she asked.

Norman shook his head. He was not tired, he was exhausted. He'd long ago lost track of the time, but he was certain he hadn't been up this late in years. It was a joke between him and Ellie that they celebrated New Years on Greenwich Mean Time since neither of them were likely to be awake when the clocked tipped over to midnight locally. Norman's hand clutched and empty glass that he didn't remember drinking from. He'd never been close to this drunk. The alcohol churned in his stomach.

"You know what turns me on?" Gina said.

Norman shook his head. He felt emptied of words.

"I love it when I know that someone really *wants* me. It's just the biggest turn on. Don't get me wrong, you're not a bad looking guy, Norm, but it doesn't matter because I see the way you look at me. It's like you don't want to admit how much you want me, but you can't contain it. It's just pouring out of you Norm, and that drives me crazy."

Norman nodded.

"I had a shrink who called it a pathology. Can you believe that?" Gina said. "He said I mistook sex for love, but I don't even know what that means. You know?" Gina had pulled a small compact out of her purse and examined herself in the mirror and frowned briefly before snapping it shut.

"I better go freshen up," she said. "You'll be okay here, won't you?"

As Gina turned for the bathrooms, Norman's stomach flipped and he was sure he was going to vomit. It was imperative that he make it outside. Nothing was more important than getting out of the restaurant before he let it go. He clamped his hand over his nose and mouth and ran, knocking into people, but even as he crested the door it came forth, spurting between his fingers out of his mouth and nose. The second and third and subsequent waves hit as he hunched over the curb. Strings of drool reached from his mouth toward the ground and the stomach acid burned his nasal passages. He couldn't bear to have Gina see him this way, but neither could he move from the spot.

After awhile he smelled her behind him, her fresh application of perfume penetrating even the smell of the upchuck. "I got sick," he said.

"Yeah, wow," Gina replied. "I can see that." After a long pause filled by only the sound of Norman spitting into the gutter she said, "Is there something I can do?" in a way that made it clear that she didn't want to do anything.

"I'll see you in the office on Monday," Norman said, never turning around. He listened to her heels click away down the sidewalk, gaining speed with each step. He remained hunched until he felt strong hands tugging under his armpits and he turned and saw the one in the lime-green sweater helping him upright.
"Upsie daisy," the man said.

■

Norman cupped the coffee mug in his hands, not yet able to make himself drink it.

"Go on," the one in the lime-green sweater said. "Drink up, you'll feel better."

They were in a diner, Norman across a booth from the one in the lime-green sweater and one of the ones that looked like just about anyone. Norman's tie was crusted with puke, ruined. He took it off and shoved it in his pocket. He'd drop it in the garbage on the way out.

"Ellie's got to be worried," Norman said.

"She's okay," the one in the lime-green sweater replied.

"How do you know?"

"She trusts you."

Norman humphed at the irony and tried a sip of the coffee. It burned on the way down and he added some cream from the little tin container on the table, swirling it through with his spoon. "So what do you want?" Norman said.

"What everyone else wants."

"And what's that?"

"The legal recognition of our bond. The state's seal on our love." The one with the lime-green sweater placed his hand gently on his partner's arm as he said this. They leaned their shoulders together and touched heads. Norman thought it wasn't a bad looking picture. He knew what that was.

"Love doesn't need official recognition," Norman grumbled.

"You're right," the one in the lime-green sweater replied. "Love is love is love. We don't *need* recognition, but we want it."

"Not everyone gets what they want."

"But why should we be denied our wants when they're the same as everybody else's?"

"Because it's not natural?" Norman replied in the form of a question.

"And who's to say what's natural?"

Norman tried to think, but his brain wasn't working quite right. It was late and he was confused and they were taking advantage of that and they kept touching each other in tender ways, which was distracting. "I'm sure there's an answer," he said, "but I just can't think of it right now."

Both of the men smiled at Norman, the kind of look you give a child, and the one in the lime-green sweater spoke. "Well, you let us know when you do. We've been waiting a long time for it."
Norman nodded. He was tired of looking at them. They'd seen what happened and that meant they reminded him of his shame. No one did any more talking. Some food Norman didn't remember ordering arrived, steak and eggs over easy, crispy hash browns that the yolk dripped through. Norman was suddenly hungry so he ate, eyes on the plate, shoveling it in. The men must've have left at some point because when he looked up, they were gone.

He slept in his car for an hour before driving home, just to make sure he was sober. At home, he showered in the dark slowly. He knew Ellie wasn't asleep when he slipped under the covers, but neither of them said anything.

The next morning, Norman slept late and when he got up and went to the kitchen he saw Ellie's back to him, scrubbing at the sink. "You hungry?" she called out to him without turning around.

He went to her and pressed against his wife from behind and she stopped scrubbing, clutching the brush in her hand. Norman paused until he felt their breathing join and he slipped one hand around front and through her robe and cupped her breast and Ellie dropped the scrub brush. Norman's other hand rested on Ellie's buttocks and then began to bunch the robe higher and with it the nightgown. He ran a finger along the inside of her thigh. Ellie sighed softly under his touch.

"What's got into you?" she said.

"Something," Norman replied.

John Warner is the author of a novel, *THE FUNNY MAN*, published by Soho Press, and is co-color commentator for *The Morning News* Tournament of Books. He hopes he's teaching writing somewhere, but he's not sure where that might be at the time you're reading this.

EXAMPLE A

CAROLINE CREW

In the story, there are five ghosts:
previous you, previous me,
and the old lovers, who bangle together
like grannies at Thursday bingo.

We should feed them.
Maybe some fruit so they recall
the quickness of flesh.

I implore you, because you insist
you are strong, to politely decline
their invitations: politely assuage
their dim bickering,

politely take their hands
and lead them to the Interstate.
Arrange their morbid fingers

to the universally thumbed sign
for 'get me out'. If we can just
get the ghosts on a truck or bundled
in the Buick of some lonely old couple,

think what would be empty, think
of the wild nothing inside our chests
and what we could say to fill each other.

We are not the truck, or the old couple,
or the fruit. In this poem,
we are just the people.

The ghosts are riding north,
and have left condensation on our hands.

SENSE OF SELF

CAROLINE CREW

The first time I saw the back of his throat
was on Nicholson Street, closing time,
shouting 'Get to fuck!' straight to my eyes
when I refused to go home.
I followed his directions. Two years
of biblically wasted days I strained

to find the road. Tried each path,
toeing the ground at every corner,
breath held for every grain of dirt
underneath toenails that might move
something, give a sign that this
 was the direction, ahead is destination.

Fuck was an untreadable distance.
He had forgotten to pave the paths
correctly. Left stones upturned,
didn't fill the small abysses
littered on each narrow way
lost to the horizon. Still, I obeyed

made sure to get to fuck some
other way, the promise of a good
woman. Applied myself to
myself, in the classroom
waiting for the slow drones
to lap against my ear lobes,

because nothing hardens the nipples
like Kristeva's abjection of everything
and outside, in parks and gardens,
rubbing myself against trees with
the hesitance of pox-ridden explorers.
And what explorer doesn't need

another pair of hands? Calloused,
and soaked in. Help carve out
new trails along clavicles,
play the keep-steady when
the hammering starts to shake
that bridge to fuck I'm building.

Caroline Crew grew up in England, went to school in Scotland, lives in Atlanta. She wrote poems in all those places, drank pilsner ales, and always made sure to explore. By the time you read this she might live somewhere else. Her work has appeared in *Anon* and *>kill author*. She blogs about poetry and things at FLOTSAM, carolinemarycrew.wordpress.com.

THE YOUNG SWORD SWALLOWER AT DINNER

KARRIE WAARALA

The restaurant is snowdrifts of linens,
clink and rustle of silverware on hunger,
low rumble of polite conversation.

The knives gleam righteous and solid here,
respectable weight across my hungry palm,
whisper a polished invitation to perform.

Father is a pompous stiff-backed chair,
his tie a snake baring its high class white fangs,
his eyes chisel warnings across the table.

I am nothing but a hasty prop, half-
hearted show of family value to the fat,
moneyed fish Father is circling greedily.

Mother is vapid moss, barely feigned interest.
I know that empty elevator look.

The knives issue their toothy challenge that sets
the moth pulse in my neck fluttering, and in
answer my fingers slither to loosen my collar.

A narrow gasp splits the talk, dissolves to
sickened splutters, Father's choked bear snarl,
see-sawed empty chairs clatter against floor.

Father, you should know better. Don't
trust me to fence with boredom for myself.
You know what weapon will choose me.

His throttle-fisted clutch at my collar bursts
the ear-ringing bliss, throat full of cold success,
my red carpet premiere, his standing ovation.

ILLUMINATED (THE TATTOOED LADY EXPLAINS)

KARRIE WAARALA

They are all here.
From the stuttering hands and sawdust mouth
of first neighbor boy all those summers ago,
to last weekend's slate-eyed butcher in Topeka,
the death of pigs still clinging to his cuticles.
All of them.

They are woven into spider webs,
braided into anchor ropes.
Pluck them from between the tail feathers of swallows,
jab curious fingers on the ones who thorn roses.

The ex-husband, with piñata fists,
bruises bursting forth and bright pain
littering the floor with every swing, yeah
he bled letters into knuckles of a learned left hook.

And the Spaniard I stole a whole off-season with.
Fingers like divining rods and sugar in his throat.
Blind as a promise.
Said he could never place the scent of my skin.
He's pollen flecks on that sternum sunflower.

Hell, even the brutal back alley whose face
I only remember as greasy smear of hate
and whose touch whittled down to
cold metal kiss against throat of
course I never knew his name.
But that's never stopped me from playing Adam.
The one I've given him lines the third tine
of the pitchfork of the devil
that rides my right thigh like rodeo sin.

And not just the epic verses are writ.
Plenty of Johns have
Jesus wept
on the pages of my skin.
Even the shortest stories deserves to be told
in ink.

The sailors, the townies,
the suckers, the shills,
the reverends, the drunks,
the ones who thought they saved me,
the ones who will never guess
I saved them.
See, there's a fee for the story
they get to sling over beers about
stolen sweaty hours with a sideshow,
a fee they never even know they're paying.
It's permanence.

I prick buzz and grind them
into this kaleidoscopic passion play,
I dagger claw and fang them
into my ever-evolving manuscript
sprouting landmine characters
and illustrations like hallelujahs,
because full-spectrum pain
is how I pray.

And this way,
none of them
ever really
leave.

Karrie Waarala is currently pursuing her MFA in Creative Writing from University of Southern Maine. Her work has appeared in *The Orange Room Review*, *Foundling Review*, *Stymie*, two national poetry slam anthologies, and on a coffee shop floor in Arizona. Karrie recently debuted her one-woman show, LONG GONE, which is based on her poems about the circus sideshow. She really wishes she could tame tigers and swallow swords.

AMERICA'S FIRST TELEPHONE DIRECTORY, ANNOTATED 132 YEARS AND 50 ½ WEEKS LATER

JOEL ALLEGRETTI

***

LIST OF SUBSCRIBERS.

New Haven District Telephone Company.

OFFICE 210 CHAPEL STREET.

February 21, 1878.

Residences.	Stores, Factories, &c.
Rev. JOHN E. TODD.[1]	O. A. DORMAN.[27]
J. B. CARRINGTON.[2]	STONE & CHIDSEY.[28]
H. B. BIGELOW.[3]	NEW HAVEN FLOUR CO.[29] State St.
C. W. SCRANTON.[4]	" " " " Cong. ave.
GEORGE W. COY.[5]	" " " " Grand St.
G. L. FERRIS.[6]	" " " Fair Haven.
H. P. FROST.[7]	ENGLISH & MERSICK.[30]
M. F. TYLER.[8]	New Haven FOLDING CHAIR CO.[31]
I. H. BROMLEY.[9]	H. HOOKER & CO.[32]
GEO. E. THOMPSON.[10]	W. A. ENSIGN & SON.[33]
WALTER LEWIS.[11]	H. B. BIGELOW & CO.[34]
	C. COWLES & CO.[35]
Physicians.	C. S. MERSICK & CO.[36].
Dr. E. L. R. THOMPSON[12]	SPENCER & MATTHEWS.[37]
Dr. A. E. WINCHELL.[13]	PAUL ROESSLER.[38]
Dr. C. S. THOMPSON, Fair Haven.[14]	E. S. WHEELER & CO.[39]
	ROLLING MILL CO.[40]
Dentists.	APOTHECARIES HALL.[41]
Dr. E. S. GAYLORD.[15]	E. A. GESSNER.[42]
Dr. R. F. BURWELL.[16]	AMERICAN TEA CO.[43]
Miscellaneous.	*Meat & Fish Markets*
REGISTER PUBLISHING CO.[17]	W. H. HITCHINGS, City Market.[44]
POLICE OFFICE.[18]	GEO. E. LUM. " "[45]
POST OFFICE.[19]	A. FOOTE & CO.[46]
MERCANTILE CLUB.[20]	STRONG, HART & CO.[47]
QUINNIPIAC CLUB.[21]	
F. V. McDONALD,[22] Yale News.[23]	*Hack and Boarding Stables.*
SMEDLEY BROS. & CO.[24]	CRUTTENDEN & CARTER.[48]
M. F. TYLER,[25] Law Chambers.[26]	BARKER & RANSOM.[49]

Office open from 6 A.M. to 2 A.M.

After March 1st, this Office will be open all night[50]

[1] Deceased.

[2] Deceased.

[3] Deceased.

[4] Deceased.

[5] Deceased.

[6] Deceased

[7] Deceased.

[8] Deceased.

[9] Deceased.

[10] Deceased.

[11] Deceased.

[12] Deceased.

[13] Deceased.

[14] Deceased.

[15] Deceased.

[16] Deceased.

[17] *New Haven Register*, founded in 1812.

[18] (203) 946-6316

[19] There currently are nine locations in New Haven.

[20] Defunct.

[21] Quinnipiac means "long water land" or "long water country." The Quinnipiacs belong to the Algonquian group of tribes.

[22] Deceased.

[23] First published January 28, 1878. The country's oldest college daily paper, now called *Yale Daily News*.

[24] "Clark Lyman Smedley, an alert and enterprising business man, is the president and treasurer of the Smedley Company and of the firm of Smedley Brothers & Company, engaged in the trucking, moving and storage business

in New Haven." Hill, Everett Gleason. *A Modern History of New Haven and Eastern New Haven County, Volume II.* The S. J. Clarke Publishing Company, 1918.

[25] Deceased.

[26] Lawyer.com has a database of 114 law firms in New Haven.

[27] Publisher of *The Poet's Dinner Table*, c. 1875.

[28] Defunct.

[29] Defunct.

[30] *The New York Times*, January 22, 1896.

THREE MEN WERE KILLED

————

Compressed Gas Explodes in a Building
in New-Haven.

————

THE STRUCTURE TOTALLY DESTROYED

————

**Panic Created Among Workingmen
by the Accident—A Section
of the City Shaken by the Shocks.**

NEW-HAVEN, Conn., Jan. 21.—Two explosions started a disastrous fire to-day in the four-story brick building at 72 and 74 Crown Street. Three men were killed. The bodies of the men were removed from the building before nightfall. The dead were:

HAUSER, JOSEPH C., machinist, aged thirty-eight years.

STEPHANS, HARBONA, bookkeeper, aged twenty-four years.

TOOF, The Rev. JOHN THOMAS, aged forty years.

The building was occupied on the two lower floors by English & Mersick, manufacturers of and dealers in carriage hardware.

[31] … and Rocking Chair Co. … and Wheelchair Co.

[32] Carriage manufacturer (defunct), named for Henry Hooker (deceased).

[33] Wooster A. Ensign, dealer in iron and steel goods. "& Son" referred to his eldest boy. Both deceased.

[34] Hobart Baldwin Bigelow, boilermaker and 50th governor of Connecticut. Deceased.

[35] From the home page of www.ccowles.com: "C. Cowles & Company was founded in New Haven, Connecticut over 160 years ago. The company has evolved from a manufacturer of lanterns for horse drawn carriages to a world-class, precision metal stamping company, producing components for U.S. and Japanese automakers."

[36]

[37] Defunct.

[38] Maker of tools for draftsmen and navigators. In 2007 a Roessler-produced brass square in good condition sold for $175. A musician and composer named Paul Roessler, who played guitar and keyboards on the Dead Kennedys album *Fresh Fruit for Rotting Vegetables*, was born in New Haven in 1958, but his website does not indicate whether he is descended from the other Paul Roessler.

[39] The company announced its failure in September 1887. Its liabilities exceeded $1 million.

[40] Four years after E.S. Wheeler & Co. collapsed (see previous endnote), this company suspended business in the wake of a strike precipitated by an attempt to cut wages by 10 to 20 percent. E.S. Wheeler was secretary of the Rolling Mill Co.

[41] Built 16 years after the publication of the first telephone directory, Apothecaries Hall 23 miles away in Waterbury is a historic landmark.

[42] Druggist. Sold saccharin tablets at the rate of $8.87 per pound—in 1913.

[43] The company did not produce pomegranate green tea and vanilla chai.

[44] Defunct. Hitchings is deceased. The Yellow Pages has 164 listings under "Grocery Stores."

[45] See previous endnote.

[46] Not a predecessor of The Foote School, an independent institution of learning for kindergarten through ninth grade, founded in 1916. The school motto is *Laete Cognoscam et Laete Docebo* ("Gladly will I learn and gladly teach").

[47] See endnotes 42 and 43.

[48] Both namesakes deceased. There are 47 boarding farms for horses in the New Haven vicinity.

[49] See previous endnote.

[50] Forerunner of the diner business model?

Joel Allegretti is the author of three collections of poems. His second, *Father Silicon*, was selected by *The Kansas City Star* as one of 100 Noteworthy Books of 2006. His poetry was the basis of two song cycles composed by Frank Ezra Levy, whose symphonic work is available in the American Classics series on Naxos. Allegretti's work has appeared in many national journals.

THE COMMENT

STEPHEN J. WEST

Speaker of the comment: female; early twentysomethings; average height, maybe shorter. Her hair is dyed several shades of varmint-pelt brown and likely inspired by a tractor pull in Southwestern Iowa, circa 1984; yet, this hairdo turns that tradition on its head (ahem) with its business in the back, party up front and elegant swoosh of mullet-bangs that rest atop red plastic Rick Moranis glasses. An oversized Cosby sweater hangs on her sleight frame with calculated abandon, its Rubik's cube pattern disobeying geometry where it bunches under the cracked-vinyl shoulder straps of a Nintendo-themed backpack. Gray stonewashed denim stretches from her Koopa shell down to her Princess Peach footwear. She peruses the indie section of the new releases in Daydreams, a comic shop in Iowa City, when, upon noticing a book titled *Gremlins*, she is inspired to share her discovery with the person she arrived with, the person for whom the comment was intended.

The person for whom the comment was intended: a tall, avian-featured male who wears his freckles with as much conviction as he does his rust-colored mop-top. Mr. Dynamite rocks *Saved By the Bell* hi-tops with all the signature features: untied white laces? Check. Fat-padded tongues pulled out at a precise 45-degree angle? Check. Flawless bright white leather? Asterisk. Here is where the homage exhibits such a honed degree of irony that even Plato would cede a thumbs up: unlike the all-white version made famous by Zack Morris, Mr. Dynamite's edition is enhanced with Warholian treatments of puffy fluorescent glitter paint. His chocolaty polyester pants are hemmed five inches too short, which, considered alongside his threadbare gray t-shirt, create a thoughtful compliment to the psychedelic explosion on his feet. His ass is *skinny*. His hands are jammed in his pockets as he studies the action figures in the display case along the back wall of Daydreams. Mr. Dynamite doesn't appear to be paying much attention to Miss Peach at the front of the store, and he's seemingly unconcerned with the other people there—including the relatively forgettable patron waiting to check out with a stack of comics and within earshot of the indie section and his Peach: the person that overheard the comment.

The person that overheard the comment: your average writer-type who gets bored while waiting in lines, even short ones; someone who thinks people are both fascinating and terrifying, and has a tendency to stare too long because of it; the person who is always trying on other people's conversations, and in this scenario, is considering the relationship between Miss Peach and Mr. Dynamite, between what people say and why they say it. He has a desire to be inconspicuous; he will miss out on critical details from time to time in his efforts to remain that way. For instance: in the situation unfolding in Daydreams, the writer-type resists the urge to turn and see what Miss Peach is specifically referring to when she addresses Mr. Dynamite; at the time, the writer-type doesn't know she's leafing through *Gremlins*, and, unwilling to reveal his interest, pays for his stack of comics and leaves the store clueless about the inspiration for the comment.

The Comment: "This is either really cheesy or the coolest thing ever."

This: noun AND subject (*Gremlins*); **is:** predicate AND linking verb connecting the subject with its complement. It is also in the indicative mood, which is normal. *But,* "is" could be considered a transitive verb in this context *if* the direct object is the relative "coolness" of the subject (*Gremlins*); **either:** indefinite pronoun; **really cheesy:** compound adjective; **or:** correlative AND coordinating conjunction; **the coolest thing ever:** a hyperbolic phrase used to describe the relative merits of anything; "thing ever" is a compound suffix that establishes value when considered within the contexts of locale, audience, loci of aural emphases in the sentence that precedes it and, obviously, the subject that is being "thinged ever." This phrase might be deployed in an effort to inspire a mutual evaluation and subsequent prescription of the boundaries of a subject, thereby fostering a meaning-rich connection with a peer. It's not always so simple. There is an inherent risk to the speaker when the phrase is attached to an adjective that represents a subjective stance, one that rends the speaker vulnerable to judgment by any number of belief systems her audience may or may not subscribe to; with the comment noted above, the compound adjective "really cheesy" balances the "coolest thing ever" upon "or," the craftiest of correlative conjunctions, a linguistic trapeze act that acknowledges uncertainty and indicates a concern on the part of the speaker when faced with the possibility that her view may not be the most popular (let alone unanimous). "Or" sits comfortably in the most unstable scenarios, and in doing so, evokes some kind of magic, or casts some kind of spell, or invites some kind of hijinks that twists the very structure, the very purpose of a sentence, morphing the subject (*Gremlins*) into an abstract concept like "coolness," represented in our current example by the modifying adjective "coolest." For connotations related to "coolest," see "cool."

Cool: anything written by James Baldwin, or whoever that guy was who wrote about being cool—or not being cool—or James Baldwin; not hot; commonly used to connote a low level of anxiety in social situations, perhaps a natural "feel for it;" not necessarily at the center of culture but more akin to the margins; confident; "cool" is definitely confident. Rule of thumb for "cool:" if you have to ask, you're not. Not, for example, returning to Daydreams to ask the counter-guy how often the indie section is rearranged—not because you're interested in what's displayed there *per se*, but more so to confirm that the comment you overheard a week prior was, as you suspect following a hasty but systematic evaluation of the new releases, in reference to *The Gremlins: The Lost Walt Disney Production*, a hardcover book that jumps off the rack at you (just as you imagine it would to anyone, especially anyone looking for something to share with Mr. Dynamite) that is, in fact, concerned with gremlins. These actions could be considered "not cool;" this, some might conclude, is "creepy."

Creepy: Two days after going to Daydreams with no other agenda than to survey the indie section of the new releases and to interrogate the counter-guy with a premeditated line of questions regarding that section of comics and your best guess at the book you believe could be the inspiration for the comment you are becoming more and more and more mildly obsessed with and following a very normal and totally casual and spontaneous conversation about some patrons who by chance *may* have been wearing a Nintendo backpack and *perhaps* had glow-in-the-dark hi-tops and were looking at *that rack right there* a week ago and say how often do these books change locations like weekly and what do you know about that *Gremlins* book *right there* was that there last week? Ok thanks. You leave the comic shop, you walk across the street, and you stop. Then you cross the street again and go back in to the comic shop and yeah haha I guess I should buy this book ha my nephew's birthday is coming up soon and he would just love something for kids like this, *look* at those funny little gremlins! He'll love them ok thanks and you quickly cram the book in your backpack and glance around to see who's watching when a week later you're in the copy shop a half block from Daydreams and *you see the neon-Zacks and the Nintendo backpack* and you are abruptly distracted from the discussion your unwitting-accomplice is having with the eyepatched counter-guy regarding the merits of black and white versus color business cards quick *look* that's them, no *them* the gremlin people *right there making copies* god what could they be copying let's go let's go and you scramble across the street and stand in the sidewalk squinting at the copy shop in the reflection of the record shop window and your unwitting-accomplice is talking about business cards and you walk in yeah yeah black and white good yeah and you are sweating and looking back across the street to see if they've left the copy shop and the counter-girl asks hey are you lookin' for somethin' and your unwitting-accomplice chimes in yeah weren't you looking for something? Then why are we here? You're distracted, do you want to go back to the copy shop to spy on them? No no haha no, spy? No let's go—why, do *you* want to go back there? No yes and you have been thinking about these people and what they said and what they might have said and what they look like and what they might be copying and the book they didn't buy and *you are the one that bought it* something that's either really cheesy or the coolest thing ever and you leave the record shop, you walk back across the street, and you stop. You linger on the bench outside the copy shop craning to see through windows plastered with advertisements and reflections of the street to wait for them god you wonder what they are copying you sweat and rub your forehead and have to walk away wishing you never heard about—or overheard about—*Gremlins.*

Gremlins: "The Lost Walt Disney Production;" "the names Walt Disney and Roald Dahl do not automatically seem to go together, like ham and eggs or Abbott and Costello;" "with the outbreak of World War II Dahl enlisted in the Royal Air Force and became a fighter pilot, battling the German Luftwaffe and surviving many dangerous missions;" "it was during this period that he began to write." "He had shared stories with other RAF men about Gremlins, mythical creatures who sabotaged flights, and now he crafted a story about the tiny creatures;" "from the moment the United States became involved in World War II, Walt Disney's studio was virtually commandeered by the Armed Forces;" "Dahl's story about gremlins couldn't have come at a better time;" "as Dahl recalled in his 1978 memoir *Lucky Break,* 'Because of the Gremlins, I was whisked to Hollywood;" "while Dahl claimed for the rest of his life that the creatures were his creation, evidence points to the contrary. Sources differ on whether or not the term was used during World War I, but it seems that talk of Gremlins was fairly common among RAF pilots in the early 1940's. A memo from the Disney company's Washington, D.C. sales manager Charles D. Feitel to Roy and Walt in Burbank, following Feitel's first meeting with Dahl, states, 'The Gremlins characters are not creatures of his imagination as they are 'well known' by the entire RAF and as far as I can determine no individual can claim credit;" "this in no way discredits Dahl's charming story or his invention of the details surrounding the origin of gremlins."[1]

---

[1] From Leonard Maltin's Introduction to *The Gremlins: The Lost Walt Disney Production, A Royal Air Force Story* by Flight Lieutenant Roald Dahl, published in 2006 by Dark Horse Books, found in the indie section of the new releases at Daydreams Comics, Iowa City, Iowa. Perhaps "really cheesy;" perhaps "the coolest thing ever."

Gremlins: a 1984 film directed by Joe Dante in which a boy inadvertently breaks three important rules concerning his new pet and unleashes a horde of malevolently mischievous monsters on a small town. The three rules concerning gremlins are as follows: keep them out of the light; never get them wet; never, under absolutely any circumstances, feed them after midnight. *Gremlins* is a cult classic of comedy horror—and in recent years, because of the growing popularity of all things retro and kitschy, it has become rather hip.

Hip: tragically, "hip" is like "cool," but somehow cooler due to its reliance on timeliness—a timeliness that requires anticipation, a kind of popular precognition that demands an obscenely short lifespan. "Hip" is the new flower of culture that blooms in its most independent margins; it wilts once it begins to set root, and until then thrives on scant popularity. If culture is akin to the fate of lemmings, then "hip" is the first to feel the unreasonable impulse to run for the cliffs. What is or isn't hip is in constant flux, and that's what makes it difficult to identify, even more difficult to prefigure, and therefore sooo sexy. Hip is analog, whatever that means. Hip is recycling—literally, visually, a search for authenticity through surprising combinations of detritus, old newly appropriated, irony materialized; like riding fixed-gear bikes to bonfire parties with acoustic guitars and banjos, drinking canned beer and cheep whiskey and listening to battery-operated synthesizer renditions of hits from other times, realizing you heard this song and saw this scene before, not in its original context of course, but in a Volkswagen commercial during the Super Bowl, which sends a shiver down your spine and a sudden feeling that the experience you're having isn't quite what you thought it was, and it might not even be your own, so you Google it on your iPhone just to make sure. Hip is a value that is as contingent as it is equivocal, like, for instance, when *Gremlins* written on the cover of a book is at first associated with the retro-chic of Joe Dante's mischievous monsters, but after reading "The Lost Walt Disney Production" also on the cover, it quickly veers toward something else entirely, a topic for moms and little kids, a thing deplorable for its mass appeal. See this in the act of weighing the relative cheesiness or coolness of something before committing oneself to it outright; the intent is couched in the delivery, the infinite array of guttural accents and mouthy pauses that grant words their meanings. Go ahead and sound it out; try on the uncertainty; *feel* the context slip from Disney to Dante; say it your way, any way you like: this is either really cheesy or the coolest thing ever, this is obsessed with surfaces and coverings, with textures and accessories, with breaking apart and repurposing, with self-reference, with documentation and self-revelation, with fetishizing fetish, with the center of everything (or the middle of nowhere).

The Middle of Nowhere: Hanson's breakout 1997 double platinum album featuring the chart topping single "MMM Bop;" for the East Coast, anywhere else; here, for you, right now; a constantly fleeting an increasingly populated oxymoronic expression of locale; in the postmodern spirit, and despite the purpose of this phrase to articulate the opposite, it might be where we find ourselves beginning any new quest for something original, for those that are still inspired, even if nostalgically, to the possibility of an authentic alternative.

Alternative: an extinct generational paradigm typically exhibited as behavior that exceeds some status quo; for the 50's see "the Beats;" for the '60's go to "Woodstock;" for the 70's hear "anything but disco;" for the 80's be "punk as fuck;" for the 90's be "in Seattle" or "anywhere but Woodstock;" for the aughts recycle the previous examples; and for the 10's, the jury is still out, which, you might take as a cop out, or as a throwaway comment that at its best doesn't work in this definition, and at its worst, like all cliché, is really cheesy.

Really cheesy: Chester Cheetah.

Cheetah: An accusation made by a pre-hip Brooklynite—meaning, someone actually born in Brooklyn—when experiencing a breakdown of integrity upon the discovery that, in the effort to secure an advantage, a person has gained access to supposedly unknowable answers, or a writer-type has decried what's wrong without giving a viable solution, let alone a working alternative.

Alternative: a currently dormant generational paradigm typically exhibited as behavior that exceeds some status quo; the conduit for change where hope sometimes thrived; like, for instance, we, the latest generation of lemmings ought to, like starving mad indomitable gremlins, rising out of order like this, a devouring horde of Dynamites and Peaches and counter-guys and unwitting-accomplices and writer-types consuming the masses with unpunctuated and unmouthed words that no one's ever even written down let alone said out loud, and no one has any idea what they might mean—yet—words that flail wildly at some teeth-clenching foot-stomping neck-vein-bulging soak-me-in-water-and-feed-me-after-midnight

Alternative:

Stephen J. West received his MFA from the University of Iowa and now lives in Morgantown, West Virginia, where he teaches writing at West Virginia University. In addition to writing essays and poetry, Stephen is currently working on a biography of an avatar he calls Crisis Shoes.

I REALLY DON'T
after d.w. lichtenberg who was after joe brainard

M.G. MARTIN

i don't remember being the size of the gnome in the garden where one would eat snails i don't remember eating the snails while the aeroplane was the thing i didn't understand but couldn't not look at i don't remember being two, but it happened to me & you too i don't remember to remind myself about the things that i've remembered to forget like: eating feces at puberty, masturbating to the image of the virgin mary, carving my under arm deodorant into the shape of a whale shark, pica pica swallow a penny i don't remember licking the sweat from behind yr knee i don't remember you i don't remember yr this i don't remember you i don't remember yr that i don't remember you i haven't forgot you i don't remember you i don't remember me remembering you i don't remember you being between my body & hiroshima i don't remember because of being not good enough i don't remember being good enough to be depressive i don't remember misnomers like *eau de toilette* i don't remember wearing toilet water on my neck i don't remember misnomers like *firecracker* i don't remember ever eating a flaming saltine i don't remember indian summers but that sounds racist i don't remember retro which was about 1993 i don't remember cutting my hair like symbolically cutting my hair i don't remember why we drive on a parkway & park in a driveway, but i'm getting out now

WHAT HAPPENS WHEN IT STARTS TO HAPPEN

M.G. MARTIN

assume the position of a migraine--
remember: it looks like the sound
of water creasing like perforated
electricity like a vacant neck it looks
like a sculpture of a paper sculpture
made of smaller pieces of paper &
sculpture like it's starting to look
like a tired form of origami flesh
assume it is an empty tray of lust
looking like a familiar zipper like a
glass skeleton that looks at you
when yr migraine is sleeping in yr
sleep so it looks like pee on yr
head it looks fortunate & strange
like the red characters that live
in a cookie like m.s.g. it looks like
m.s.g. & a fever & a small anxious
metallic make believe precipice &
yr first kiss & the opposite of
opposite like where you stand now
a place further from redundant
than yr migraine it looks like it is
saying: let's touch noses

M.G. Martin is the author of *One For None* (Ink 2010.) His work has appeared or is forthcoming in *ZYZZYVA*, *Explosion Proof, Requited,* and *elimae*, among others. M.G. lives in Brooklyn, is from Hawaii, and has a dog named Ihu. Find him at www.mgmartin.tumblr.com & @themgmartin.

TWO DRAWINGS

SIOLO THOMPSON

Artist's Statement:

As an artist I am obsessed with capturing small, beautiful pieces of everyday life. My focus on figurative art attempts to describe the accidentally elegant gestures and poignant, transient beauty of the people around me. Every life is full of stories and armed with my pencils and brushes I try to find those stories and give them life on a canvas.

In This Issue
'She was suddenly, casually beauitful'
(Girl eating noodles)

'With that small gesture, she moved the world'
(Girl exposing her neck)

Siolo Thompson is a fine artist and editorial illustrator based in Seattle, Washington. Her work is primarily figurative and narrative in nature. She loves overcast weather, experimental fiction, and animals with short legs. She also designed the cover for Ethel Rohan's *Hard to Say*.

SNOW JOURNAL, DAY 46

KEVIN O'CUINN

Winter hung over us like a gaol sentence, a punishment for daring to stay. Though we all had reasons for gravitating north, no one spoke of such things. When we spoke it was of food, or of what we saw in the fire, but never of before.

The days held us tight, compressed into dim mid-morning light. We used morning's window to set and check traps, to drop lines through the ice. The fish never bit till it was almost dark, till we could barely make out what they were. We called them names we'd learned when young—cod and halibut, salmon and cabillaud—but naming things was not our game. Fish were fish, and grilled or boiled or smoked was how we distinguished them. Smoking them meant we could keep a stock, though we tired of picking wood from our teeth.

The traps stopped nothing larger than arctic rabbit, soft to touch. We skewered the meat and turned it in the fire, fried the giblets in an iron skillet. We stewed the bones and sucked out the marrow, washed it down with broth. Nothing was wasted. The skins kept us as warm as we could hope to be.

For distraction we read the flames, blue and gold and pink and orange. We sat so close, peering ever deeper, that our faces grew red and darkened. Salmon danced and wolves sang, and we threaded the images and spun tales across the night. Our early stories ended in triumph, the late ones in tragedy, revenge and betrayal. But only one story began with the figure of a girl. We each relayed what we saw, and pieced together her history, as she lay there, buoyed in the flames; her eyes black, her hair coal. We didn't blink for fear that we would lose her. A day passed, then two, and still we sat at the fire, inhaling her voyage and swallowing her fate. Someone said she was a Legong dancer, from somewhere down in Indonesia. She held her hands just so, pointed and contorted in the pyre, and never once looked back at us. She turned, finally, enough that her pointed globes shone at us. That was when the knife was pulled, a rusty blade that cut through our group. When the knife fell to the floor, two were dead and Bow had lost an eye; and the fire was dead, and all it held.

We didn't fish that morning, nor the day after; we tried, but each time we lowered a line, her face shimmered on the water. We feared what we would draw from below.

Kevin O'Cuinn lives and loves and works and plays in Frankfurt am Main. He is fiction editor at *Word Riot.* Links to his work can be found at www.kevsville.blogspot.com.

FACIAL DEFICITS

JOANNE MERRIAM

The first successful hand transplant recipient refused to take his immunosuppressive drugs, his body rejected the hand, and it was amputated at his request. Newspapers quoted him as saying he was "mentally detached from it." Another man who received a penis transplant after losing all but a half-inch of his own had it cut off after fourteen days, not because it didn't work (he could pee standing up by then), but because of what the doctors referred to as "a severe psychological problem of the recipient and his wife." I still went ahead with the facial allotransplantation surgery.

"Count backwards from ten," the anesthesiologist said, and I said, "Ten. Nine. Eight. Seven." If I said six or five I don't remember. I remember the blue pajamas everybody was wearing, and the device the surgeon had attached to his glasses that looked like a miniature telescope, and that's it. I woke up covered in bandages and nauseated.

The week before I had made myself a lemon meringue pie. It's my favorite dessert, and possibly my favorite food. I love the brightness of the yolks. I love zesting the lemons into a small mixing bowl, their bright yellow grains like pollen against the glass. But when I put the lemon against the grater I couldn't disfigure its surface and I started to cry. I understood why, of course; it was perfectly obvious to me; but I wanted my pie, too. I made myself zest the lemon and then I baked the pie and then I ate a bite and my damaged tongue couldn't taste it just like it hadn't been able to taste much of anything since the accident, which was somehow always a surprise to me, and I went to the bathroom to vomit. I threw the rest of the pie in the garbage, along with the scalloped glass pie plate, a wedding gift from Parker's decrepit great-aunt Gert. Before the accident, Parker would have been pretty mad about that, but only let some drunk smash your face against a dashboard leaving you horribly disfigured and you too will discover that you can do anything, and nobody will say a word.

"I think I'm going to throw up," I remember I said, and a nurse injected something into my IV. She was a skinny black girl in pink scrubs. "Thanks," I said, and she patted my hand and said, "just call if you need anything." In the hand she patted was a little box with a button on it, which was attached to the bed by a long cord. Presumably the button, when pushed, would signal her to come back. I hoped nobody she loved would ever have to go through this.

At the party to celebrate my new face, Grace said to me, "You look great. Really natural." When the car caught fire, my face was burned off. My nose and jaw had been pulped by the dashboard, and what was left of my face was a mess. A hot mess. Ha.

In comparison to before, of course I looked better, but I had a mirror and I knew it didn't look natural. It looked like I'd been left in the sun too long and started to melt. They'd go back in later to remove some of the extra flesh and skin. Grace was trying to be kind, of course, but she didn't understand. I didn't care that I looked kind of weird, so I didn't need to be convinced that I looked normal. I had a nose and a whole jaw again, not to mention palate, teeth and parotid gland. It was nice to have too much face for once. I tried to smile at Grace, but the nerves under the transplant were barely starting to respond, and I couldn't be sure if it looked like anything. I'd practiced smiling for an hour that morning, watching myself in the mirror, but the effect was entirely hit or miss.

"Have another drink, Grace," I said, and I made her a brandy Alexander, her favorite. I knew all my friends' favorite drinks; we were all famous drinkers. In the time it took me to pour the crème de cacao, cream and brandy into a cocktail shaker, she'd gotten ensnared by one of Parker's stories along with six other women. I dusted some ground nutmeg across the top of her drink and handed it to her.

Parker was talking about the time he went on a vision quest (he can't ever just get high; it has to be spiritual). I know this story back to front. He told me it on our first date: he went out to the forest with an ex-girlfriend of his, who was part Cherokee, and she gave him some LSD and took him to a clearing, where they lay on their backs and looked at the stars. The girl told him the Cherokee believed you could find out who you were through a vision quest, and she was going to show him who he was. He saw a coyote in the sky made of stars, and the coyote's body was made of clouds, and he went to sleep. When he woke up, the girl had left him there and driven back to the city. He had to hitchhike back and when he arrived, he went to the girl's house and she told him that she'd said she was going to show him who he was, and she had. He was the kind of guy who gets left behind. He was the kind of guy who dumps a girl and then trusts her when she offers him LSD. He was the kind of guy who thinks a coyote of all clichéd things is his spirit animal. (I guess I married him because I'm the kind of girl who likes coyotes.) Parker always tells this story like it's the funniest thing in the world, and everybody always laughs. "She was so angry when I broke up with her," Parker said.

"Aren't you going to have one?" Grace said, shaking her drink.

"Can't," I said.

"She couldn't stand losing face," Parker said, and then he noticed me on the periphery of his little crowd, and his face crumpled into an expression I can't quite describe, somewhere between remorse and the social horror one feels when one mentions something unmentionable. I tried to smile, to show I knew he hadn't been talking about me, but I don't think it came across. I don't know what he saw instead of a smile, and for the first time I wondered if I hadn't been better off without a face. I watched him toss back a finger of Maker's Mark.

I'd told the investigators it was the other driver's fault. They never caught him, so it wasn't hurting anybody. I never mentioned the drinks we had before the accident to anybody. I was just as drunk as Parker, after all, and I'd long known that it was our mutual appreciation for a well-told lie that made our marriage work.

Joanne Merriam is a Nova Scotian living in Nashville, where she works with surgical otolaryngologists and experts in facial plastics, although any mistakes in this story are her own. Her fiction has appeared in *The Fiddlehead*, *Per Contra*, and *Strange Horizons*. You can find her online at joannemerriam.com.

BUTCHER'S BLOCK

THOMAS DEMARY

The age of the crowd on the boardwalk undulates from old to young. Time gerrymanders the demographics as the sun sets, as the sky burns. Two boys fist-fight along the shoreline; a combatant collapses to his knees by an uppercut to his jaw. Outside the Taj Mahal, police cyclists surround a pack of teenagers; an old man quivers behind the authorities, his shriveled finger points at the kids in accusation. Bronzed college boys in popped polo collars hurl wolf-whistles at young girls, their bikini tops and jean shorts exposing floral tattoos on thighs and lower backs. I gawk at a black boy, five or six years old, as he slaps ice cream from his mother's hand. "Bitch," he says to his mother. His mother.

I walk into a random souvenir shop, its overhead lights beam through keychains and shot-glasses: cheap, touristy pieces to help rewrite the visitor's memory of Atlantic City. Behind the counter, outrageous cigarette prices are written on irradiated sheets of card stock. A thirty percent markup. He grins at me, a twenty-something with barbwire tattoos around his arm. "Got some new tee shirts toward the back," he says. His breath reeks of beer. He ogles the young girl fondling the tee shirts.

Her breasts are space-age. *Sugar* is printed on the buttocks of her red shorts. I can smell the ocean in her blonde hair, her skin is blotchy from hours under the sun. *Owen* is tattooed on her right hand, its cursive font is ornate, Elizabethan. She picks up a black tee-shirt: a male stick figure stands before a female on all fours. The phrase *Choking Hazard* is underneath the picture. She hands it to me without saying a word. I press the shirt against my body. "How do I look?"

She replies, "Bald black man with a gray beard. Sad eyes. A porno shirt. I should take you to a club."

Images of disco balls and rainbow lights flood my brain. I haven't been to a club in decades. Times have changed, I'm sure of it. I ask her about the tattoo.

"Oh, this? I got it about a year ago. My son."

"Why on your hand?"

She rummages through her purple pleather purse. "You'd think its stupid. It is stupid. I mean now it is."

"Tell me," I say, "unless it's too personal."

She pulls a small, amber tube from the purse. Unpainted fingernails twist until waxy lip balm rises. Her bottom lip is split; she grimaces as the balm seeps into the wound.

"Is it too personal?"

"No. Well kinda. But not that kinda personal. I'm right-handed, so—when I punched someone—I wanted to remember who I was fighting for. Like I said, it's stupid."

"Are you a boxer?"

"No," she said. "I punch people."

"For fun."

"No," she said, throwing the lip balm into the bag. "Sometimes, a bitch gotta fight. Is that stupid?"

"Does it matter what I think?"

"It's stupid."

"I didn't say that."

"You don't have to. I know it. I'm a mother. I'm supposed to be grown, right?"

"It's all relative," I say. "How old are you?"

"Nineteen."

I wave her off. "Whatever."

"Seriously." She dives into her bag and hands me her license. "And you?"

I stare at the plastic card. Alexis Keane. She withheld her smile for the camera; a gash was under her left eye. Her hair was slicked into a ponytail, quick and dirty, as if she left some boy on the couch. I swipe my thumb across her photo two, three times. "Older," I finally answer.

We had Jean late in our marriage. Ten years together before we decided to try. Our family was a master plan: travel, settle into our careers, buy a home, have one child. I wanted a son. When I held Jean in my arms for the first time, I fell into amnesia.

While Eva attended her weekly painting class, I rested my head on the kitchen table. In the dark, drowning in liquor, my eyes tried to hide. Jean entered and sat next to me. She poured herself a drink, swallowing and handling the bourbon's singe with a honed, matured sigh. She said, "Tits aren't everything, Dad."

It was on a Tuesday when Eva called and asked me, with an unnatural nonchalance, to meet her at her doctor's office, to "swing by" as if picking up a bottle of wine on the way home. "Some news," she said.

"Can you be more specific?"

"Yes, but not over the phone."

I hung up on her without another word. Some news. She called while I sat in entangled traffic on the Walt Whitman Bridge. I boiled in my car, air conditioner in need of repair, with the windows down and a rorschach of sweat stained the back of my shirt. Under my breath, I called her a cunt and, at once, cursed myself and apologized as though she was in the passenger seat.

Eva was not at the doctor's office; the bricked, one-floor building was dark, its parking lot empty. At home, I parked the car and peeled myself from the seat, my skin and spirit covered in a tangible stickiness, like the adhesive left behind from a bandage. Eva was at the dining room table.

"What the fuck?" I asked and repeated, "What the fuck?"

"I figured you were in traffic," Eva said. "But I thought you'd make it in time."

"Why did you even call me? Don't do that shit to me," I said.

"They found a lump," Eva said, "in the right one."

"A lump?" I leaned against the wall and stared at the hardwood floor. "What did they say?"

"I need a biopsy. And that's why I called. I didn't know your schedule, you know, if you had meetings or needed to travel this week. You were running late, though," Eva said with a tinkle in her voice, the sound of fragile crystal beginning to spider-web with fissures, "so I scheduled it for Monday. I asked if it was okay to wait until Monday. They said it was fine. I guess if it's cancerous, what's a few more days going to do to me?"

I frowned and asked, "How come I never felt it?"

"Because my love," she said, "the left is your favorite. Isn't that a silver lining? The favorite one stays?"

■

"You should get a tattoo," Alexis says. She folds the pizza slice in half and rams it into her mouth. When she speaks, the half-chewed food is a beige paste fed to prisoners and astronauts. "I can take you to my spot, up past Trump. Best tattoo parlor in town."

"Maybe I don't want one. Besides, I wouldn't know what to get." I rip a napkin into little squares and ask, "Does it hurt?"

"It's a needle stabbing you a few hundred times per minute. Then again, you're straight once the endorphins kick in. Get one on the neck."

"Doesn't that scream 'mid-life crisis'?"

"It's all relative," she says with a smile. "How old are you?"

"Fifty-five."

"Oh, you're past mid-life. Unless you live to be a hundred. I wouldn't want to live that long. What's your name, by the way?"

"Ellis. And I'd kill to live another fifty years. At some point, you cross over. The scales tip and you wake up, realizing the majority of your years are behind you. I guess one way to cope is do outlandish things: bungie-jump, skydive, get gored by Spanish bulls."

"Fuck girls half your age."

"Well yeah, that's obvious. A cliche, really."

"No more than getting a tattoo."

"Point taken," I say, nodding my head as if it's oversized, plastic and attached to a metal spring. "I'm trying not to be obvious."

"Sitting with a young white girl, a P.Y.T., a tenderoni—you're failing, Ellis."

I look around. The sun is gone and a breeze blows off the ocean. Couples sit around us, elbows and beach towels resting on white tables. They slurp through straws and glance down at cell phones. A girl holds one up, showing her partner a video clip of a fat black girl dancing on a table, then tumbling to the ground like a trash can. I can't see the video, but I remember the sounds—remember how hard I laughed when Jean emailed it to me. I light a cigarette. "How old is your son?"

"Three."

"Where is he?"

"With my mother."

"Why aren't you with him?"

"Cuz it's my birthday."

"Is it really?"

"You saw my license, didn't you?"

"I didn't notice. Happy birthday. Where's his father?"

"In jail."

"For?"

"Murder," she says. Suddenly, she releases a maniacal laugh, rubbing her hands together like a mad scientist. "Drugs, actually. Possession," she says while reaching for my pack of smokes, "with intent to distribute. Stupid. You should buy me something—for my birthday."

"I did. I bought you dinner."

"Pizza and soda. Yeah, I'm swooning over here." Alexis points a thumb over her shoulder, "The mall's still open."

On the way, a juggler performs in front of a Korean War memorial: a statuesque soldier, eight feet tall, clutches dog tags in his left hand. The bedazzled pins twirl, suspend themselves in the air, freeze in time until their master calls them down. I watch the angles, the geometry, the choreography of his hands. It requires the same motion, the same speed and placement. No deviation or the illusion will come crashing down on the boardwalk. Alexis tests his concentration and asks him his name.

Choreography unfazed, he replies "Rob."

She asks, "How long have you juggled?"

"Ten years, something like that."

"This is how you make money?"

"Nope. I'm a lawyer." I find myself impressed. I drop a five dollar bill into his Phillies ball cap. "Thanks, brother," Rob the juggler says.

The oceanside mall harbors high end boutiques. In the jewelry store, Alexis stands over a glass case, staring at the assortment of engagement rings: chunky or solitaire, clear or multicolored, set into yellow gold, white gold or platinum prongs. She softens a little bit, just enough for me to peer past the breasts, the sugar on her ass, to finally see her true age. Nineteen and longing for marriage—she wants the fantastic clarity of a husband, a lifelong partner, a bedtime story. Her neediness betrays the act of an old soul, of a weathered spartan, of a mother.

The night before Jean left for college, Eva came out with it. The crickets sounded their mating calls. I watched an arrowhead of birds begin their flight south. With my bourbon and cigarette, I felt at peace and, therefore, expected something to go wrong.

Her silver hair was cropped short with tight, pea-sized curls. She grabbed my glass and sipped; the porch light reflected off the bourbon's surface, bounced into her eyes, and consorted with the hazel inside her irises. "I want a divorce," she said.

I didn't know what I wanted. Earlier in our marriage, I imagined her leaving me, as a child imagines the death of a parent. Preemptive preparation in the hopes that the inevitable cut would miss the bone. I said, "I still love you."

"But you don't want me. Anymore."

"I just need some time to adjust."

"It's been long enough," she said. I looked at her. The last chemo cycle was in the past; it and the butcher's block halted the cancer's progress. The color in her face, the shade of butter pecan ice cream, returned. She put on some needed weight. Still in repair, but almost back to full power: she was in love. The way she stared across our yard, out toward the starless sky, affirmed what I once imagined.

I took medical leave to be with her. For two years, she skulked about the house; her gold bracelets clanked as she ambled from room to room, in search of food or companionship, her haunting work conducted at night. As her health improved, and the deeper scars started to heal, she wanted more of me—in the old ways.

We acted like virgins. As I shifted underneath the sheets, Eva walked into our bedroom, her arms folded across her chest. I wasn't ready. She pulled the knot loose and the white robe fell. The half-erection I worked up evaporated. I sutured my eyes closed, covered my mouth and wept. Her incision had the slightest curve upward, a wry smile. Eva stood there, naked and incomplete, gasping as I turned over and switched off the lamp.

"Tell me about him," I said.

They met at her painting class. Younger, but not too young. "Late thirtyish," she said. He asked for a cup of coffee and time to explain cubism. She hesitated for a moment, as though she started to share sexual details. In her mind, I stopped being a husband, and became a confidant, a chum, an old girlfriend.

"Talk to me," she said.

"About?"

"How you feel."

"How—I—feel." My fingers dug into the patio chair. "I'm being punished." I stopped to swallow the salted knot in my throat. "I'm being punished for being honest." Who lied to me? Who whispered the nonsense into my ear? My mother? The minister who married us? Daytime television?

I smashed the glass onto the floorboard. "How I feel," I said, pointing to the mess. "I hope it eats you alive. I hope they take the other one. Finish the job." Eva said nothing. She blinked a few times, her eyelids shuttered a few tears loose, and she rose, walked into the house and slammed the red front door shut. The words looped in my head, echoing off some cavernous part of my brain, and I glanced down at the pool of bourbon, motionless and austere like crime scene blood.

Alexis steps back from the engagement rings. "I'd never get married," she says.

"Not the wifely type?"

"I don't see the point." She removes a cell phone from her bag and presses a few buttons. The small screen sets her face aglow and, like that, the light disappears. "What's the point?"

"How would I know?" Alexis lifts my left hand, her thumb grazes the tan line around the ring finger, and looks up at me. "It has its pluses and minuses," I say.

"No doubt." She kisses my fingertip, licks it as though she were Sharon Stone. I can feel the saleswoman judging me from behind the counter. Standing there, hands on narrow hips, watching the obvious.

■

I don't know what to think. It's not as big as I imagined and it's packed. Painted freaks of nature, with plastic things in their earlobes and metal hoops and studs pierced in rather inventive places, roam around the small tattoo parlor.

We plop down on the blue sleeper sofa; it smells of corn chips. Alexis quickly fills out the consent form. I look over my form and slowly, neatly, print my name, age, mailing address, and check marks inside of empty "No" boxes: am I HIV positive, do I have allergies, am I currently under the influence. I lean over and ask, "Do you mind going first? You know, so I can see an example."

"You're scared," Alexis says.

"I'll pay for it. My birthday gift to you."

"You don't have to buy me anything." Alexis takes our clipboards, and driver's licenses, to the receptionist: her hair is dyed red, a steel ball juts from her bottom lip—the dot of an exclamation point. Alexis hands me my license and drops onto the couch. "It'll be a little while," she says.

"Seriously. The tattoo's on me. Nothing too expensive, though."

She turns to face me, her leg underneath her body, half Indian style. "So you're really having a mid-life crisis."

"No. Just facing facts, trying to accept who I am, learning to digest regret."

"So it doesn't get easier as you get older," Alexis says while biting her fingernail.

My laugh is a foghorn; the patrons turn their heads, either scowling or staring blankly like paper dolls. "I'm sorry," I say, still chuckling to myself. "No, not easier. You just—accept that there'll never be enough time to get it right. Stumbling around at nineteen is the same at fifty-five, except slower, more arthritic."

"I regret having Owen. Sometimes. I sat outside the clinic, freezing my ass off in my shitty car, thinking up reasons why I shouldn't go through with it. I took a gamble, I think. I said, 'Alex, you'd regret killing this baby more than anything else.' What is that, a premonition? Maternal intuition?"

"A good eye," I say, half-believing in the worth of my words. "Maybe that's why you don't want to get married. You see something, even though you can't articulate it right now."

"I lied," she says. "About marriage. Something about it seems comforting. It reminds me of a blanket. It gets warmer as it gets older, even when it starts to smell moldy." Alexis tilts her head, lays it on my shoulder and superimposes her hand on top of mine. "Let's get married," she says.

"Polygamy is illegal here," I say.

"We can pretend."

"I'm too old," I say.

"I'm not playing games with you," Alexis says, "if that's on your mind."

"What do you want from me?"

"Nothing," she says. "Isn't that enough?"

God, I want it to be enough. I feel nothing for Eva, but it's not enough. Kisses on her mouth, widening myself to receive her bad days, watching Jean make our old mistakes in novel ways: I can't make love to my wife anymore—but what of making time? We'll never fuck again, yet I still burrow my nose into her silver hair. I can only give her half intimacy or, perhaps, the frustration of an orgasm unrealized. She has a right to more. An amicable severance does nothing to temper my anger, my fright. She's leaving me with thirty years' worth of memories; I have no room in the basement to house so many boxes. The lump left me cleaved, too—but it's not about me.

Some guy walks up to us. I almost piss my pants when I see two horns, I don't know what else to call them, stretching underneath his forehead's skin. His right arm, well defined, is a mosaic of symbols and faces and numbers. His smile is amiable, well-versed in customer service training, and he asks, "Who's up first?"

"Me," Alexis says. She leaps from the couch and grabs my hand.

"Back here." He ushers us down a narrow hallway, an art exhibit, its walls covered with random photos of fresh tattoos. Overhead, three purple light bulbs add a soothing contrast to the ruckus: the laughter, the loud rock music, the buzz—stop—buzz of tattoo needles jamming themselves into skin. We walk straight ahead—the usher peeking back at Alexis as she leads me by the hand—until we enter the room at the end of the hall. "Shut the door," he says to no one. I follow orders.

The tissue paper crinkles underneath her body. Alexis sighs as she reclines in the white chair that resembles those in barbershops and dental offices. The room is as clean and nauseating as bleach. "I'm DJ," he says over the snap of plastic gloves. "Did I do you before?"

Alexis pouts her lips and nods slowly. "I think so. You look familiar, now that you mention it."

DJ chortles to himself, his face aglow with achievement. "Something on the other hand this time?"

"My neck."

"Maybe," I say, watching their heads whip toward me, "that's not a good idea. Maybe," I say as I approach Alexis, "here." I trace her collarbone. "A little more personal than the neck, I think."

"That'll work," she says. "What should I get?"

"My name." I laugh. She stares me down. "I'm joking."

"Ellis," she says, facing DJ. Without a cue, Alexis removes her tee shirt. Her breasts are netted behind a plain white bra. She continues to stare me, while pointing to the blank slate of skin next to a bra strap. "His name is Ellis."

Getting older is a type of time-traveling, moving in and out of past lives and loves, projecting oneself into the future, bleak and accurate as it might be. The dystopia I see whenever I close my eyes: buildings are dilapidated and blood-splattered, graveyards buzz with new business, and love loses touch with sex.

We'll sit on the bench of a beach house and watch the ocean's black turn purple, a deep amethyst, then orange and, finally, blue again as the sun returns. Seagulls will land on the beach and squabble over yesterday's trash. I'll glance down at my wrinkled hand and feel something familiar in my chest as her smooth hand comes into view, lands on top of mine, and interlocks fingers. *Owen* will look faded.

I'll visit Eva in the hospital. We won't speak. I'll hold her hand and watch the screen: a black background split by a green line. I'll continue to carry that weight while she disintegrates into a feather. I'll kiss her forehead, stroke her face, whisper in her ear. A flicker of warmth will come over her before the chill emerges.

Alexis stands over me, shirtless, my name branded onto her chest. Whole and made anew by ink, she runs her hand along my damp scalp. The chair is comfortable. The light hurts my eyes. I can't see a thing. Not a goddamn thing. I hear DJ ask me, "So whatchu want?"

Thomas DeMary, whose fiction has appeared in *Up The Staircase*, also contributes a weekly column for *PANK's* blog. He currently lives in southern New Jersey. For more information on the author, visit him at www.thomasdemary.com.

SONNET, WITH BIRD

SHERMAN ALEXIE

1. Seventeen months after I moved off the reservation, and on the second plane flight of my life, I traveled to London to promote my first internationally published book. 2. A Native American in England! I imagined the last Indian in England was Maria Tall Chief, the Osage ballerina who was once married to Balanchine. An Indian married to Balanchine! 3. My publishers put me in a quaint little hotel near the Tate Gallery. I didn't go into the Tate. Back then, I was afraid of paintings of and by white men. I think I'm still afraid of paintings of and by white men. 4. This was long before I had a cell phone, so I stopped at payphones to call my wife. I miss the intensity of a conversation measured by a dwindling stack of quarters. 5. No quarters in England, though I don't remember what the equivalent British coin was called. 6. As with every other country I've visited, nobody thought I was Indian. This made me lonely. 7. Lonely enough to cry in my hotel bed one night as I kept thinking, "I am the only Indian in this country right now. I'm the only Indian within a five thousand mile circle." 8. But I wasn't the only Indian; I wasn't even the only Spokane Indian. 9. On the payphone, my mother told me that a childhood friend from the reservation was working at a London pub. So I wrote down the address and rented a lorry driven by one of those cabdrivers with extrasensory memory. 10. When I entered the pub, I sat in a corner, and waited for my friend to discover me. When he saw me, he leapt over the bar, and hugged me. "I thought I was the only Indian in England," he said. 11. His name was Aaron and he died of cancer last spring. I'd rushed to see him in his last moments, but he'd passed before I could reach him. Only minutes gone, his skin was still warm. I held his hand, kissed his forehead, and said, "England." 12. "England," in our tribal language, now means, "Aren't we a miracle?" and "Goodbye." 13. In my strange little hotel near the Tate, I had to wear my suit coat to eat breakfast in the lobby restaurant. Every morning, I ordered eggs and toast. Everywhere in the world, bread is bread, but my eggs were impossibly small. "What bird is this?" I asked the waiter. "That would be quail," he said. On the first morning, I could not eat the quail eggs. On the second morning, I only took a taste. On third day, I ate two and ordered two more. 14. A gathering of quail is called a bevy. A gathering of Indians is called a tribe. When quails speak, they call it a song. When Indians sing, the air is heavy with grief. When quails grieve, they lie down next to their dead. When Indians die, the quail speaks.

Sherman Alexie is the author of, most recently, *Face*, poetry, by Hanging Loose Press, and *War Dances*, poems and stories, by Grove Press. He lives with his family in Seattle.

LIMIT TEXTS MATTERING: 99 TWEETS

LANCE OLSEN

1.   Begin with a question:

2.   What can the novel do that film, TV, the internet, and the Xbox can't?

3.   One answer: eat them: David Foster Wallace, Mark Danielewski.

4.   Another: explore the resonant complexity called human consciousness through an extended space and time: Faulkner, Woolf.

5.   Another: revel in what a sentence might be, and do, and why, and how: Barthelme, Beckett.

6.   Vladimir Nabokov.

7.   Such authors are the reason any film adaptation of any serious novel has always-already failed before the screenwriter types the first word.

8.   But also this: due to its length & plasticity, the novel can investigate certain sorts of architectures that other genres can't.

9.   Which is to say, as José Saramago noticed, the novel is not so much a literary genre as a literary space.

10.   Or Milorad Pavic: Nonreversible art (think a piece of music) is made to be experienced linearly from start to finish.

11.   Reversible art (think sculpture) can be entered at various points, wandered through or around without a sense of beginning, middle, or end.

12.   We tend to think of the novel as nonrevesible art when in fact it is the other thing.

13.   The joy of the novel genre is that it has never figured out what the hell it is.

14.   Which is to say: the novel contains architectonic potential that such forms as the pop song, the painting, the poem simply can't imagine.

15. R. M. Berry. Lidia Yuknavitch. Vanessa Place.

16. All you need to do to understand my point is remember the first time you opened Raymond Federman's *Double or Nothing*.

17. The rush of bodily immediacy you felt.

18. *Double or Nothing* or Kathy Acker's *Blood & Guts in High School*—important, not just for *what* they are, but for *how* they are.

19. Which is to say: language was suddenly *mattering* on the page, words becoming images becoming figures becoming birds.

20. And this, too: Federman's every layout innovation executed with a typewriter.

21. With a typewriter.

22. Each page turned into a stage as well. A canvas. A visual problem.

23. Which is to say: making that part of the novel we have forgotten to see into another mode of delivering meaning.

24. The technological reality of the page, Ronald Sukenick used to refer to it as.

25. Habitualization, Viktor Shklovsky once writing, devours work, clothes, furniture, one's wife, and the fear of war.

26. When Roland Barthes announced the movement from work to text, N. Katherine Hayles arguing, he was both prescient and blind.

27. Prescient because he was instrumental in expanding our notions of textuality beyond the printed page to fashion, menus, street signs, sex.

28. Blind because the vocabulary of the text had the effect of eliding differences in media and genres.

29. Hayles' point: the medium in which a text is instantiated *matters.*

30. Or this: the difference between art and entertainment:

31. Art deliberately slows and complicates perception so that one can re-think and re-feel language, narrativity, experience, & media.

32. Entertainment deliberately speeds and simplifies perception so that one doesn't have to think about or feel very much of anything at all.

33. If you don't use your own imagination, Sukenick pointed out, somebody else is going to use it for you.

34. Boredom, Guy Debord pointed out, is always counter-revolutionary. Always.

35. Once upon a time, we already knew these things, then that changed.

36. Re: art: to make objects "unfamiliar," to make forms difficult, to increase the difficulty & length of perception.

37. Shklovsky commented.

38. In 1916.

39. 157 years after *Tristram Shandy*.

40. Ergodic literature, Espen Aarseth said, is that which requires nontrivial effort on the reader's part in order to traverse a text.

41. Which is to say I couldn't have written my novel, *Head in Flames*, without knowing Federman had written his.

42. David Markson his.

43. Carol Maso, Joe Wenderoth, Mark Danielewski: thank you.

44. Musical mattering.

45. Where words are what they say, but also how they say and how they look.

46. Nonergodic being that where the effort to traverse the text is trivial, with no extranoematic responsibilities placed on the reader.

47.   Except, for example, eye movement and/or the periodic flipping of pages.

48.   Media Specific Analysis: materiality reconceptualized as the interplay between a text's physicality and its signifying strategies.

49.   A repositioning of critical inquiry that entwines instantiation and signification at the outset, Hayles' point being.

50.   A line from Urs Allemann's *Babyfucker*: I fuck babies.

51.   The postmodern in art, Jean-François Lyotard suggesting, would be that which puts forward the unpresentable in presentation itself.

52.   How, through its sheer force of impossible content, Allemann's line gains materiality on the page.

53.   The varieties of mattering in the omnivorous novel alone.

54.   *I fuck babies* becoming an impossible sculpture about how language languages.

55.   Lyotard: That which searches for new presentations, not in order to enjoy them, but to impart a stronger sense of the unpresentable.

56.   Or this example, from another register entirely: Jen Bervin's breathtaking artist's book, *The Desert*.

57.   Which takes John Van Dyke's 1901 prose celebration of the American wilderness & sews across 130 pages of it in light blue thread.

58.   Leaving another text entirely in her wake.

59.   Making the almost-language behind the fluvial zigzag stitch there and not there and not not there all at once.

60.   Text texturing into meaning.

61.   Text mattering as a reaction against mass reproduction and textual disembodiment.

62.   Or postliterate, asemic writing: language without specific semantic content, forms whose meaning is the vacuum of meaning.

63.   The present absence of meaning. Marco Giovenale. Henri Michaux.

64.   Writing that becomes more powerful for the very reason that it can't be read, quite, although at first glance it feels like it can.

65.   Writing that matters without sense, matter as form sans substance, which is in fact the substance: a xenolinguistics.

66.   Or Christian Bök composing a text translated into a gene & integrated into a cell so that the text gets "expressed" by a bacterium.

67.   Which, in response to this grafted, genetic sequence, will commence manufacturing a protein that is itself another text.

68.   I hope, Bök elucidating, to engineer a primitive organism as a useable machine for writing.

69.   Consequently, by remediating the written through the organic, mattering William Burroughs' axiom: language really *is* a virus.

70.   Let's wonder for a moment why we don't refer to Christian Bök as a novelist.

71.   Why we *do* refer to Steve Tomasula's hypermedial project, *TOC*, as a digital novel.

72.   The technological reality of the page mattering in Tomasula's meditation on time precisely because it isn't *mattering* anymore.

73.   Which is to say, along with Hayles: digital media have given us an opportunity we have not had for the last several hundred years:

74.   The chance to see print with new eyes, and, with it, the possibility of understanding how deeply literary theory & criticism . . .

75.   Have been imbued with assumptions specific to print.

76.   Reverse remediation: books becoming more like computers even as computers become more like books.

77.   Even as reading speed on a screen is typically 28% slower than on a printed page.

78. Which is to say: Limit Texts, you could call Tomasula's, call Bök's, call all of these, each within its specific medium.

79. Texts that take various elements of narrativity to their brink so that we can never think of them in quite the same ways again.

80. Which is to say: how some books, once you've taken them down off the shelf, you can't put back up again.

81. Michael Joyce's *Afternoon: A Story.*

82. Ben Marcus's *The Age of Wire and String.*

83. Young-Hae Chang's *Traveling to Utopia.*

84. Books are not going the way of the dinosaur, Hayles emphasizing, but the way of the human.

85. Changing as we change, mattering as we matter: Facebook, DNA, the horror film, Wikipedia, Twitter.

86. *Grenztexte,* after Karl Jaspers's notion of *Grenzsituationen.*

87. Literary moments, that is, accompanied by acute anxiety, in which the human mind confronts the restrictions of its existing forms.

88. Acute anxiety & acute freedom, both.

89. Moments that allow us to abandon, however fleetingly, the securities of our limitedness & enter new realms of self-reflective consciousness.

90. Which is to say: meaning as meaning, but structuration—mattering—as meaning, too.

91. Meaning re-imagining meaning as a spatial, media-specific phenomenon.

92. Architectures of possibility—sans, to be precise, the architecture.

93. Because writing that moves toward the edges is always more valuable than that which remains in the center.

94. That tells us what we already know in ways we've already seen.

95.   Because such limit writing asks us to envision the text of the text, the text of our lives, and the text of the world other than they are.

96.   Offering us brief instants in which to contemplate the opportunity of fundamental, radical, liberating change in all three.

97.   Just.

98.   Like.

99.   That.

Lance Olsen is author of twenty books of and about innovative fiction, including, most recently, *Calendar of Regrets* (FC2, 2010) and *Head in Flames* (Chiasmus, 2009). He teaches experimental narrative theory and practice at the University of Utah.

WHITE SPIDERS

HELEN VITORIA

My eyes will become white spiders on his clothes. I will watch beads of sweat form on his upper lip and on his forehead. He will begin to sweat on the clothes as he is folding them, and the clothes will be soaked from sweat till he will have to re-wash load after load, of polyester security guard uniforms. I will picture him naked and unsafe, until he feels it. Then I will prepare to leave and before I sashay my way to the door. I will turn and say: *It was great seeing you again.*

Helen Vitoria lives and writes in Effort, Pennsylvania. Her work can be found and is forthcoming in many journals including: *elimae*, *Mud Luscious Press*, *>kill author*, *Poets & Artists Magazine,* and *Dark Sky Magazine*. Her chapbooks: *The Sights & Sounds of Arctic Birds* and *Random Cartography Notes* are both available as e-chaps from Gold Wake Press, 2011. She has been thrice nominated for *Best New Poets Anthology 2010*. She is completing her first full length collection: *Corn Exchange*, with an expected release Fall, 2011. Find her here: helenvitoria-lexis.blogspot.com/

MY MOM'S GETTING PLASTIC SURGERY

COREY GINSBERG

Tonight on the phone, my mom tells me she's getting plastic surgery, and I'm not sure what to say because it's weird to think of my mom as a candidate for a facelift because she's not Anna Nicole Smith or a Kardashian or an instillation art exhibit, and besides, her face is the face I reconstruct when we talk from our bipolar country corners, it's the face that used to drive me to swim practice at four a.m. and sit in the car while I lap-after-lapped and bring me donuts before school, it's the face I've seen twist into every combination of swear words and sometimes apology as my adolescent asshole self told her I hated school and I hated life and I hated her goddamn fucking face so now that I don't hate her goddamned fucking face I don't know if she should change it because I'm used to her wearing it just like she's used to me wearing that stinking rotting hoodie she bought me when I went away to grad school the first time and she's seen it on me so often she begs me to get a new one, tells me she'll give me the money if I'll please just go shopping but I don't want a new hoodie and I don't want her to have a new face, and her offer makes me feel extra bad cause it leaves me wondering if I had the money, would I give it to her to get her face did or save it for that inflatable bounce house I plan to get for my thirtieth birthday party, which she better come to, new face or not, and better bounce in, because if she gets her face lifted she won't have jowls anymore that would flap when she bounces, and maybe if she had the surgery she won't call me on those drawn-out nights when my dad's out of town as she channels her third vodka solipsistic assonance about how she's droopier than our Basset Hound, how that shithead got *his* eyes done when they sagged so much the vet had to do emergency surgery so why the hell can't she be more special than the dog for once and I'm annoyed because I don't know what she wants me to say so instead I ask what they do with all the extra skin because in my writer mind I'm imagining a huge quilt of lady necks and liver–spotted flabby folds pastiched into some sort of modern art cannibal canvas and it freaks me out because I've seen *Face Off* enough times to know how wrong things can go in face surgeries and she could come out of the operation with taut spandex cheeks clinging to the scaffolding of her skull or looking like Connie Chung or some other stranger and the face she'll be staring out from won't be the one that used to *oogle google* my brother while he laid drooling in his crib, it won't be the same face that used to *fishlips crosseyes* my sister from the front window while she walked home from the bus stop, and I'm worried that when they revise her face, trimming and tightening the second draft, that her new dust jacket will forever take the place of the original.

"HER HOUSE IS PEPTO-BISMOL PINK," MY NEIGHBOR SAYS

COREY GINSBERG

Look at that asshole house on the corner. See that eyesore? Yeah, take a look the cement box twat on that burnt-out lawn. Wonder who lives in the taint of this street. Bet it's some Barbie Doll icing hooker. Bet she collects flamingos and parades them on Valentine's Day. That house over there, it's tongue pink. It's a 1987 Boy George hypercolor nightmare. Good thing I've got on big aviator sunglasses. That's one slut of a dwelling. Makes my labia hurt thinking about it. Cirrosis of the senses. Could be the bastard stepchild of Mr. Bubble and Tinkerbell. Check out that shriveled soul of the captain of the cheerleading squad. I used to have Chuck Taylors that color—when I was six. Spit your gum out on that cotton candy sexpot. Gas station carnations, that hole is. There's a douchebag in my friend's fraternity who wears shirts that shade with the collar popped. That's some tacky kitsch bullshit festering on this swatch of land. We should call someone about it. Dear officer, arrest the foreskin of Miami. I've seen discharge from a unicorn that's more subtle than that house.

Corey Ginsberg studied creative writing at Florida International University. Her work has most recently appeared in *The Cream City Review*, *Front Porch*, *Memoir(and)*, *The Writer*, *The Los Angeles Review*, and *Subtropics*, among others. She currently lives in Miami with her toothless dachshund and works as a freelance writer.

DEAD APPLES

ELAINA SMITH

The tiny town of Dunlath hadn't had a woman in its midst for well over fifty years. It repelled anyone not already living there, with its crumbling buildings and fetid smell of decay. Trash lingered in corners and gutters, while any wildlife had long since fled. Few trees still bloomed in its arena, while grass grew brown and ragged no matter the season. As the years passed, the town produced male child after male child, without a female to stem the torrent. The mothers quietly left, one by one, until only men remained. A few of the men raised the issue of the town dying out due to the female exodus, but the older residents simply shrugged when asked while continuing to suck on their pipes. The subject eventually drizzled away like the men's pipe smoke, until it was never brought up again and then forgotten completely.

The town had little difficulty adapting to its woman-less state. The need for sex shriveled as the men aged, and many forgot what a woman was even like. Thoughts of slender curves, soft skin, and soprano voices evaporated from the inner workings of their brains. By the time fifty years passed, most had not thought of a woman in forty-nine of those years. No one attempted to leave the town to find female companionship. Women were forgotten entities, symbols of a lifetime since passed. Content with their town's bizarre makeup, Dunlath's citizens quietly whiled away their lives, until one day a woman appeared among them.

A relative of the old doctor's—who was an oddity in the town, for he had not been born in Dunlath—the young woman had recently graduated from college with few prospects for steady employment. Knowing that her uncle's health was tenuous, she packed her bags and moved in with him under the guise of becoming a volunteer housekeeper. The doctor had initially hesitated when she had presented her idea, warning her that Dunlath contained only men. "No women?" she had asked with a laugh. "How is that even possible? You can't have men without a woman somewhere." After listening to her many protestations combined with incredulous laughs, the doctor eventually capitulated to his niece's demands.

The woman arrived on a muggy day in summer. It was late afternoon, but the sun still hung as a blurry mass low in the sky. Setting her bags in the entrance-way, the doctor introduced his niece to his closest neighbors, both middle-aged bachelors with leathery hands and ragged fingernails. The woman held out her hand in greeting, but the men refused her handshake with eyes downcast and mutterings unintelligible. They then quickly scuttled away into their houses, doors squealing in their frames. The neighbor across the street was of a similar gender and disposition, with tufts of gray hair spiking from his brown-spotted head and a surly frown creasing his face. Upon her tour of Dunlath, the woman noticed that the owner of the grocery store was also a man; so was the owner of the drugstore, and the clothing store, and the gas station. Men lined the park benches and the restaurant booths. Men drove the cars and rode the bikes and walked the street. They were like a flock of wrinkled, gray crows, crowding every space with their ragged feathers and cracked beaks, pecking and squawking at one another.

It was upon entering the sole clothing store that the woman began to believe her uncle's warning. The tables were neatly stacked with collared shirts in neutral colors, while ties made a circle of cheap silk on a nearby stand. Pleated trousers, belts, and hats fanned out to the edges of the store; belts tangled together on one rack while suspenders swung from another. The store's name was noncommittal—CLOTHES, someone had decided to call it decades ago—and the woman had been told pointedly that it was the only place that sold apparel in the entire town. As she ran nervous fingers across racks of gray slacks without a skirt or blouse in sight, the few men in the vicinity watched her openly. One slowly sidled up the length of the rack she stood at, his tongue wetting his thin lips in spurts like an albino lizard. She turned and fled.

It took a week before the woman gathered the courage to venture out again. But fear spiked her mind and constricted it with every gaze that lingered upon her as she walked outside. The men stared at the woman with wide eyes and sometimes gaping mouths as she walked the town's two mile radius. She could feel their gazes follow her every move, would glimpse white faces peering through upstairs windows whenever she left the doctor's house. Curtains shivered in the sudden departure of their owners whenever the woman looked into a window; and when she looked away again, she knew fingers curled the curtains back again, and the eyes resumed their watching.

Both the middle-aged and elderly hankered for a look and perhaps even a whiff of a being unknown to them. They followed her from store to park to her home; their jobs were forgotten upon sighting her. Her lips were the plumpest and reddest lips they had ever seen in their lives; her hair was thick and glorious. When the air whirled as she walked past them, they all inhaled. They watched her in the doctor's living room, walking to and fro, her hips swinging and her breasts bouncing. She enticed. Where once there was nothing, suddenly lurid images filled all of the rotting brains of the townsmen the moment that female entered their town. But while they followed her with their eyes and dogged her footsteps, not one touched her or spoke to her. Her femininity burned too brightly for their eyes; she was, to them, *too alive.*

The woman tried to ignore the stares: she quickly realized that making eye contact with the men was usually the best way to send them scuttling like beetles into dark corners, allowing her a moment's peace. The only man who didn't bother her was balding Mr. Greer, the owner of the grocery store. Mr. Greer was quiet and unassuming by nature and could never bring himself to stare blatantly at the woman when she came to his store. He would shuffle away from her when she came within ten feet of his presence, turning red each time. Once when she passed by him in the condiment aisle, Mr. Greer dropped a glass bottle of ketchup, shattering it across the gray tile. He dropped boxes and bottles and bumped into tiers of cereal and cookies at least once a week, sometimes more depending on the woman's need for particular items. Mr. Greer had more cuts and bruises and destroyed merchandise than he had ever had in all of his sixty-three years when that woman began coming to his store. But it was always with a little frown that he would close the store on the days when she hadn't come at all.

■

One afternoon after her weekly sojourn to the grocery store, the woman pulled an apple out of her basket for a quick bite. The fruit was pale red and lacked shine, but the meat inside tasted pleasant. The woman very rarely ate while she walked in public, mostly because the men seemed to stare at her more intently than ever as she bit, chewed, and swallowed. But now her stomach rumbled insistently, and she took a large bite of her apple, her white teeth flashing in the sunlight. Her tongue lapped the fruit piece into her mouth. But something interrupted the woman's intent to chew—the footsteps of one of the men behind her, the opening of a window upstairs—no one ever knew. She gasped and then choked on that piece of red apple, the same color of her lips, and it lodged in her throat. It cut off her air, and she collapsed, right there in the street, apples and oranges and pears rolling from her basket every which way as she struggled for air.

Two men, Mr. Young and Mr. Old, saw the woman collapse. They watched across the street as her lips turned blue and her throat constricted around the apple piece. When she seemed to be near death, they approached with heavy steps. Mr. Young poked her in the side with the toe of his mud-encrusted boot. "Is she dead?" he asked.

The woman shuddered.

Mr. Old shook his head. "Not yet."

The woman shuddered one last time before going still. Mr. Young poked her again, but she made no response.

"Guess she is now," he said.

After a few more pokes and prods from both sets of boots, Mr. Young shambled his way to the Doctor's house, while Mr. Old stayed with the quickly forming crowd of people. The news of the woman's collapse traveled like a virus; soon a ring of men surrounded the woman on the ground. They bent their old bodies toward her like gnarled trees bent by the wind, but no one attempted to move her or to touch her.

The doctor ran to his niece; Mr. Young meandered behind him, whistling a random tune. He pushed through the crowd of men and checked his niece's vitals, searching for a pulse and feeling for any air leaving her lungs. He listened to her chest, but her heart had stopped. He attempted chest compressions, but no life returned. She was dead. Her lips were blue, her breath still, and the offending fruit was still wrapped in her white hands and the piece still lodged in her throat. You could see its bulge stuck in her airway.

The doctor wiped sweat from his upper lip. "Could someone help me carry her home?" he asked the men surrounding him.

Everyone hemmed and hawed in perturbation. They couldn't touch her, they mumbled amongst each other. It was only until a yellowed sheet was procured that the men were grudgingly willing to help carry her. The doctor wrapped her up like a mummy, and he and two others carried her to his home, the woman's white hand swinging limply as they walked.

Days passed with the woman lying still on her uncle's paisley sofa, not breathing or moving. But for some reason no one could fathom, she never began to decay—she remained cool to the touch but never stiffened in *rigor mortis*. Her lips remained their red, red color, as if blood still flowed through her body. The doctor, in consternation, took her pulse and listened for her heartbeat multiple times a day, but could never find either. She had no breath but looked like a sleeping figure. She remained the same for a week, a life-size doll decorating her uncle's living room. The doctor found it unsettling, seeing his dead niece lying prone and unmoving every morning as he got his morning coffee and read the paper. Knowing he couldn't bury her, he instead bought a glass coffin and placed her inside it. This allowed him to monitor her without committing the impropriety of having a dead body lying out in the open in his living room.

Upon hearing of her placement in the transparent coffin, the men began gathering at the doctor's for viewings. It quickly became a favorite activity, for the men were able to get close to the woman without her making eye contact with them. They could watch her without the fear of her reacting or—God forbid—speaking to them. One by one, each man in the town visited the woman in her glass coffin that stood in the middle of the Doctor's living room. The crowd became so large after a week's end that many of the men demanded that the coffin be placed in the park instead.

"I can never see her when I want to," Mr. Collins complained to the doctor. "I don't get off work until 5:00 and you shut your doors at 5:00! How's a man to see the woman with you doing that?"

The doctor hesitated but eventually agreed to let the coffin be placed in the park, mostly because he was tired of having his house filled with people every day. It was not a particularly picturesque place, Dunlath's park: it hadn't been mowed in years, and the grass sprung up in crevasses like nose hairs poking out of nostrils. The trees were barren and dry, with the occasional leaf growing on a branch before falling to its doom. But put the coffin in the park they did, right under the old barren willow tree. Its dry branches brushed the glass of the woman's tomb tenderly when a breeze would blow through. And it was every day and almost every hour that at least one man would come to gaze upon the woman in her glass coffin. She became the main attraction of a town that had not had anything of interest happen in decades.

Mr. Old and Mr. Young (now the stuff of legends for having seen the woman collapse) traveled to see her around their lunch hour, bringing their ham sandwiches and bottles of warm milk with them to the site. They would sit on one of the splintered benches and gaze upon the un-decaying woman for their entire lunch hour, as they chewed and swallowed their sandwiches with robotic simultaneity. Sometimes they would even stroke the glass with the tips of their wrinkled fingers, leaving streaky prints on the coffin's exterior.

"She's a beautiful thing, isn't she?" Mr. Old said. "Looks like a doll."

Mr. Young always agreed with a nod as he made little fingerprint swirls around the woman's head. They hovered around the coffin after they finished eating, sometimes touching the glass, sometimes just staring at the woman encased within. When the town hall bell tolled 1:00 PM, both would sigh and trundle back to work, their empty lunch pails swinging in unison.

Mr. Greer, the grocer, was not quite so obvious in his fascination with the body. He had been desperate to see the woman after her collapse but could never bring himself to view her in the daylight hours. It was not until she had been moved to the park that he was able to see her again. That first night, he waited until the crowds had dispersed, usually around the 9:00 hour when night had settled completely. At 8:30, he combed the little patch of hair still left on his head, shaved the bristles on his chin, and donned his best suit—a suit over twenty years old and a size too small. The pants were a bit tight in the gut, but Mr. Greer would never have worn anything else to visit the woman. Suit on and hair combed, he left his dwelling across town, making certain to close the door without it creaking. He scurried down the main thoroughfare of the town, conscious of the few lights still burning in some windows. He arrived at the park within twenty minutes, sweat dampening his pits and brow.

Grass crunched under Mr. Greer's shoes as he approached the coffin with mincing steps. The wind whistled sadly through the willow branches, which tapped across the glass surface of the coffin like fingertips across a piano. When he stood over the encased body, he realized that the woman was truly lovely, lying dead in the moonlight. Her hands were folded demurely in her lap, her black lashes spread across her cheekbones like little fans. The moon touched her hair with silver highlights, and her lips and cheeks seemed rosier than ever. Mr. Greer gazed upon her with a week's-long hunger. He had missed the tap of her shoes upon his store's tile, the movement of air as she passed him, the smell of her as she walked by. He had loved when she smiled, showing her little, pearly teeth, or when she frowned when reading a food label. He watched her now, openly and without fear; his eyes darted across her face, drinking in her white complexion, her red lips, her sharp cheekbones. Her ears deserved worship; her nose adoration. Mr. Greer's gaze never left the woman until dawn began creeping upon the horizon. It was only then that he hastened away, promising the woman he would come again that night.

That next night, and many nights thereafter, Mr. Greer visited the woman, always looking but never touching. He loved to see how her skin turned pearly under the moon's light; how her fingers continued to be folded so sweetly in her lap. How her eyes remained closed to the world. It was only when the moon began to wane that he gathered the courage to touch. The darkness enshrouded his desires and hid them from the world. When the half moon hid itself behind the willow, Mr. Greer placed the fingers of his right hand on the cool glass of the coffin.

The very tips of Mr. Greer's fingers were the only part of his body to touch the glass in the beginning. But as his courage grew and the night darkened, he began petting the glass like a lover. Up, down, across, back, and forth, he petted the coffin and marked it with his moisture. He felt his skin begin to tighten around his body, constricting his veins. All the while, he watched the face of the woman. He wondered if she truly were dead but thrilled that she was unaware of his watching her. His eyes darted across her body, from her lips, to her nose, to her legs, to her belly, to her breasts, hungry and fearful. His blood throbbing even more, he began to trace the line of her lips. His finger followed the line of her top lip, that little dip, the fullness of her bottom lip. His brain whirled and his thoughts congealed into a mass of glutinous sensuality. His groin grew heavy with blood congealed. Fear engulfed him, and he fled the woman early that night.

Mr. Greer traced other parts of the woman as time progressed, only the glass separating them. That first night, it was her lips. The next, her eyelashes. His fingers followed the line of her throat and then her waist. He eventually reached her hips and then her thighs. Her calves followed and then her feet and toes. It was only when the new moon caused the park to be a land of black shadows that Mr. Greer was at his most courageous. When only a few flickering streetlamps provided any illumination, Mr. Greer began tracing the woman's knee. But his index finger was rebellious that night: it traveled from her knee to her thigh, stroking that line. His finger continued to move, up, up, up, to a place he had always avoided but had begun thinking about ever since *that* night. He had wondered what it felt like, what it looked like, what it smelled like, but never had thought to trace it. This night, his finger followed the line of her inner thigh and fell upon her genitals, her vagina, her cunt.

Mr. Greer froze then and began to wheeze. Sweat poured down his face. Trembling, he tried to lift his finger but his other three fingers merely splayed themselves on the glass like a wrinkled spider. Blackness began to stick to his corneas and faintness weakened his body. He imagined he could feel her warm cunt below his hand and the thought overwhelmed his brain. The smell of it filled his nostrils. His hands slid from the top of the coffin as he fell to his knees in supplication. Seconds later, he collapsed.

■

It wasn't until morning that someone found Mr. Greer. His face was smashed into the ground, his glasses crushed, and his arms pinned beneath his gut. It was Mr. Collins who found the grocer on his way to work. Mr. Collins came to see the woman every morning: he would usually do a quick survey of her body, making certain she hadn't moved in the night before whistling off to his office. No whistling occurred today—instead there was only huffing and puffing as Mr. Collins pushed Mr. Greer onto his back. He stuck his fuzzy ear to Mr. Greer's chest only to hear a soft heartbeat.

"Can't believe he's still alive," muttered Mr. Collins. "Looked as dead as the woman there." Mr. Collins began lightly slapping his fellow citizen, all the while telling the man to "Wake up, wake up, I'm going to be late for work!"

Mr. Greer slowly regained consciousness. The sunlight fractured into a thousand stars through the view of his shattered glasses. Blinking, he looked up into the leathery face of Mr. Collins.

"What happened?" he asked with a croak.

"Dunno," Mr. Collins replied. "Think you might've had a heart attack or something. What were you doing out here anyway?"
A hot redness crawled up Mr. Greer's face. "Nothing."

Mr. Collins harrumphed.

Struggling to sit up, Mr. Greer wheezed a little before adding, "Nothing, it was nothing, really..."

It was at this moment that the two began to attract the attention of a few onlookers. Mr. Collins stood and brushed the grass off of his trousers. "You can take care of yourself now," he said before walking away. Mr. Greer eventually made it home with the help of a few others. After changing out of his stained suit, he left for his store. It was two hours later than when it normally opened—7:00 AM—and the crowd converged on the grocer with impatience. "Where you been, Greer?" a patron asked. "I needed my pack of smokes an hour ago and you just get here?"

Mr. Greer shushed the commotion and bounced on his heels in an attempt to soothe. "I'm sorry, overslept, you know," he explained. He fumbled for his keys to open the rippled glass doors to his store. The moment the doors parted the crowd winnowed its way through, paying no attention to its owner. Quickly, though, the word spread about Mr. Greer's collapse in the park.

"Did you hear?" Mr. Lloyd said to Mr. White. "Found right in front of the coffin—Mr. Collins was sure he was dead!"

Collapsed in the park in front of the woman and her coffin—what was he doing there in the middle of the night? the gossip swirled. Mr. Greer felt the accusatory stares as he mopped aisle five that morning. He knew that glaucoma-glazed eyes stared at him between the lines of canned vegetables. While straightening aisle one, patrons sidled by him with their gazes following his every movement. The breaking point came when Mr. Hall, one of the youngest men in the town at the fresh age of fifty-six, stood and stared at Mr. Greer across a row of lemons. Mr. Greer abandoned his store right then, everyone watching him as he walked out.

Despite his collapse earlier, Mr. Greer still readied himself to see the woman that night. He waited even later to leave—at about 2:00 AM—donned his wrinkled and grass-stained suit and quickly made his way down the back alley of his home. He slinked behind trash cans piled high, scared skinny cats rummaging for scraps, and arrived at the coffin in the park. Under the faint light of the streetlamps, Mr. Greer saw that the woman seemed a bit paler, a bit less rosy in her cheeks and lips. Her skin no longer glowed, and her hands seemed limp. The bulge in her throat protruded against the skin even more than it had yesterday—a lump marring the smooth surface of her white skin.

Mr. Greer moaned. He knew she was dying, that she was leaving him behind. She would die completely and be buried deep underground, in a place he could not get to. Her body would decompose, the flesh melting from her bones as maggots ate at her. And then she would turn to dust, and Mr. Greer would have lost her completely. The image of her skeleton caused him to scrabble at the glass of the coffin like a dog scratching to get out of a locked room. He couldn't find the latch to open it at first. He dropped to his knees and searched with the touch of his fingers, but found no way to get to the woman. He had to save her. She was so beautiful to him, so precious in her repose. He eventually found the edge of the glass and lifted the cover with a groan of exertion. The hinges screeched in protest but the coffin surrendered to the old man's demands. And there she was before him: no longer could glass separate them.

He almost expected her to begin moving as the air curled around her. But the woman remained as still as she had been the day she took a bite of her apple. Mr. Greer felt hot tears rise in his eyes as he gazed upon her sickly pallor. Even after choking on that apple, she had still seemed so alive in her unconsciousness. Now death was taking her completely in its grasp. Impulsive and desperate, Mr. Greer began to lift the woman out of her coffin into his arms. He knew that he was her savior, the only one who could help her.

She was cold and her head hung lifelessly across his arm. Mr. Greer wheezed a little at her weight and swayed as he began walking away from the park. He didn't know where he was going, but he had to take her away from this place. She was wonderful; his mind wrapped itself around her existence and squeezed. Shuffling and puffing, he slowly made his way onto the cobbled street and stopped a moment to catch his breath. His head pounded and he began to feel similarly like he had that night he had touched her cunt. Dizzily, he began to walk again but tripped on a loose pebble in the street. He lurched forward, and the woman rolled out of his arms and hit the ground with a smack of skin on stone.

Mr. Greer began crying harder.

He couldn't get up; his arms hurt and his legs were on fire. His lungs expanded until they were close to bursting, and all the while, tears streamed down his sunken face. He wiped them away with the back of his hand. He began crawling towards the woman, the buttons on his suit scraping against the cobblestones. When he reached her side, he realized that she was moving—moving in little jerks like she was having a seizure. And beside her face lay the apple piece, finally free from the confines of her throat.

■

Tabitha Crowne had lived an unexceptional life: she had a lazy childhood, an easy adolescence, and a breezy college experience. She had majored in psychology, with no notion of how she would use it for future employment. Her test scores and papers earned her C's but never A's. She was neither particularly intelligent nor particularly beautiful. Her one boyfriend had always forgotten her birthday and their anniversary but had been too indolent too smack her around. Her life had brimmed with apathy and boredom. It was Dunlath that had brought her feelings never experienced: at first it was fascination with the odd little town. The fascination quickly shifted to fear of its queerness. And the fear eventually became outright loathing.

For loathsome were the men of Dunlath, who were shrunken within their bodies and similarly shrunken in their minds. They wheezed and they huffed and they snorted and they spit whenever she walked past them. She could hear them walk up behind her when she sat on park benches, when she inspected fruit in the grocery store: the tips of their wrinkled noses would brush her skin and she would shudder at the remembrance. Some of the younger ones would follow a line up her ankles to her navel, eventually fixing their gaze on her breasts but never going higher. They could never look her in the eye. It was the day she had bought that apple that Tabitha had decided to move as far away from Dunlath as possible.

But now she became conscious of lying on street cobbles, her body throbbing. Her throat burned, and she coughed in heaving gasps. There was little light, and she tried to get her bearings. Her mind was a whirl. Turning on her side, she saw a man staring at her, his face shiny with tears.

"Who are you?" Her voice was painfully hoarse, and she coughed in little gasps.

The man inched closer to her, and suddenly she recognized his visage: the grocer. He had been the only man who wouldn't stare at her openly. But now, he was gazing at her with a raptness that bordered on worship. Eyes wide and mouth agape, Mr. Greer at first couldn't even answer her simple question, the answer to which she already knew.

Tabitha tried again. "Where are we?" she said.

Mr. Greer didn't immediately answer. "We're in the street," he eventually replied.

"But, why?" Tabitha watched as the little man came closer and closer to her, until his hands were inches from her face.

Mr. Greer's tears increased down his face. "I was saving you. You were dying."

Tabitha closed her eyes against his expression. "Mr. Greer, why would I have been dying?" Her voice was still hoarse but she no longer felt the impulse to cough. Her body still throbbed in pain; she wiggled her toes and flexed her hands to get the blood flowing, just a little.

"It was the apple," Mr. Greer replied. He stared at her face even more closely, and then reached out to touch her throat. Tabitha pulled away but he didn't notice. He began stroking her. "The apple, that was here. You choked, and we saved you by not burying you. But then you were dying, so I was taking you away so we could be safe together."

Tabitha could only register the feeling of his sweaty fingers touching her throat. Her heart began beating faster.

"I'm fine now." She slowly sat up, her palms placed firmly on the ground. "I'm all right now, right?" The wrinkled hand had moved from her throat to her face.

"You were so pretty in that coffin! I would come every night to see you, did you know that?"

Mr. Greer leaned in until their noses touched. Tabitha instinctively recoiled, but lacked the strength to fully pull away. The old man began kissing her lips, wet kisses that made her stomach roil. His saliva dribbled down her chin. He moaned and huffed against her, and she pressed her hands against his chest. It wasn't until he began to fondle her breast that she gathered her strength and rolled away from him, her stomach to the street. The two watched each other, one aroused, the other afraid.

"No," Tabitha whispered. She got to her knees and wobbled. Mr. Greer reached for her, his hands outstretched. She slapped them away. "Don't touch me!" Wiping her chin of his assault, she added, "Just leave me alone."

Her tone seemed to startle Mr. Greer. He backed away from Tabitha and watched as she slowly got to her feet. She swayed a little but was able to stay upright. "I never wanted you to save me," she said.

Tabitha staggered down the street, away from Mr. Greer, who remained kneeling on the cold cobblestones. She staggered in front of houses beginning to awaken as dawn approached. She caught herself against lamp posts and benches, her breath heaving. She walked down the thoroughfare of Dunlath as the entire town of men watched her from their windows. And it was when the sun shone high in the sky, that Tabitha Crowne made her way out of that town, alone. She crossed its threshold and never looked back.

Elaina Smith was born and raised in Missouri but has been fortunate enough to live in California for a few years here and there. She graduated from the University of California, Santa Barbara with a degree in English and a random minor in Japanese, which she has yet to actually use in Japan. Writing crazy fiction is her escape from her boring life as an office worker. She currently works as a fiction editor for *Revolution House Magazine* and loves reading new work from talented writers.

ON THE LACK OF PARANORMAL ACTIVITY IN MY APARTMENT

MATTHEW MAHANEY

Sometimes I wish ghosts were real, and that I had one haunting me, especially when I have people over and the conversation starts to falter. My ghost could whisper conversation topics in our ears or just scare us so we actually go outside and do something for a change. I guess my wish could seem offensive to people who believe in ghosts, but believing in something doesn't make it real. Maybe ghosts are kind of the opposite of God that way. I know a lot of people who wish they believed in God, but I've never heard anyone say they wished God was real.

THIS WAS BEFORE

MATTHEW MAHANEY

The coming thundersnow kept us busy waiting. Picture your average summer afternoon storm, then make the air forty degrees colder, the bullets of warm water against every windshield sticky white flakes. The thunder and lightning are the same. Thundersnow. This was the day after she dreamt of me as a blood-stained jackal on the outskirts of the Serengeti, which was two days after I dreamt of her as a block of ice puddling into sidewalk cracks, blurring the scales of large grinning fish drawn in blue chalk by our children. This was before we had children.

Matthew Mahaney was born in one place, grew up in another, and has since lived in several more. He currently lives in Tuscaloosa, where he is an MFA candidate at the University of Alabama. Other poems appear or are forthcoming in *Blue Mesa Review*, *Caketrain*, *Everyday Genius*, *Jellyfish*, and *Sentence*, among others.

IN THE AFTERLIFE, WE ARE FLAMINGOS

KAT SANCHEZ

I am a brain surgeon in my dreams
And then I am not
You are all the birds behind me at the zoo

In a photograph from 1991
I also stand on one leg and think hot pink

I am visiting you in a hospital bed on an island
I am exotic and so are you
You are flying back to the mainland

And then you are not

I took a trip to New York and wanted to be
Your lawn ornament

I wanted to be your pink velveteen couch
And the glassware pinking as the Brooklyn sunset

Skipped through the windows
Of your garden apartment

I wanted to be the plastic twinkling lights
Hung along your walls

We are animals like a goat in this life
Whose four legs are clinging and clacking
To the wall of a cliff

We write each other postcards and letters with
More postage than usual

We have tried being as sad as possible
We have tried being not in love with everything

Kat Sanchez migrated from southern California and now lives in the windiest city. She is the layout and design editor for *Fifth Wednesday Journal* and has poems published in *Denver Syntax*, *Poets and Artists*, *Columbia Poetry Review*, *OVS Magazine*, and others.

INCEST DREAM, OR SLAM POEM FOR E

MILKS

I had sex with my cousin. It was a dream. Sorry.

I had sex with my cousin, who is from a different walk. She is in the mud, while I am two floors up with three degrees and cats with special diets. We are both poor.

I had sex with my cousin, who is black; I'm white. Or she's biracial, but identifies as black, or has Gone Over to the Dark Side, as my mother has said. My mother says the same thing about me, because I am a dyke, and scary, though she chooses different language. I am not, actually, poor.

I had sex with my cousin, who is fat. She has three kids by different fathers. She is in and out of jail, of rehab. She stutters. Her mom is mean. Her nose is always running. We're the same age, born the same year, slept in the same bed at our grandmother's house when we visited as kids. She was and is a heavy breather. We are the only girls of eleven cousins, thirteen if you count our uncle's two adopted sons from El Salvador but we don't because our parents don't.

I had sex with my cousin. We're talking father's side of the family. My cousin's mom, or my father's sister, or my aunt, is a manager at Wal-Mart and a seasonal school bus driver. My cousin's father left before or after she was born. I can't say if my aunt expected him to stay. I can't say if child support has been arranged or given. One of my cousin's mom's three brothers, my cousin's uncle, my father, earns six figures. Another of her brothers, my and my cousin's uncle, is a millionaire. The third of her brothers, my and my cousin's other uncle, who adopted the two refugees from El Salvador, lives quietly on a small smelly farm from which he sells chickens and eggs. Possibly he's gay. Possibly my cousin's mom is also gay. My cousin's possibly gay mom and our possibly gay uncle are the black sheep of the family. They're both fat. The millionaire uncle is also fat; nobody calls him that.

I had sex with my cousin, who has stolen checks from my grandmother and made them out to herself to support her drug habit, I guess. This interpretation comes from my mother who gets it partially from my grandmother, my mother's mother-in-law. My father, whose family it is, can't be bothered to call.

I had sex with my cousin, whose first kid, whose name my parents make fun of, idolizes me because I gave him undivided attention for a few hours once when he was four. I'm told he's been asking for me ever since, which I understand could lead someone like my cousin, or my aunt who is my cousin's son's primary caregiver, to pretty deeply resent me.

When I had sex with my cousin it was two years since I'd seen her, a few Christmases ago and she'd had her new baby with her, a daughter whose name my parents have not bothered learning. I had been having a stilted conversation with her about her shit job at a gas station when my millionaire uncle interrupted to ask me about graduate school. I turned from her to him like a dog smelling power and so enabled an insipid conversation that spread to the whole room. Nobody asked my cousin anything. Nobody asked my aunt anything. Nobody asked my probably gay uncle anything, except to be mean ("I see you've been eating well?").

I had sex with my cousin whose mom, my aunt, is pretty butch and maybe gay, and my mother has suspected that growing up in a sexist family full of catered-to men made her Want To Be a *Guy*, and I wonder if this is her theory about me, and I wonder if this theory could be partially right, and I wonder so what if it is, when I'm having better sex than she is.

When I had sex with my cousin, it was shortly after my learning that she'd been pulled over for driving without a license, or for some crime that had to do with driving that also involved her driving without a license. Because she didn't have a license, she didn't show them her license. When the cops asked for her name, she gave them mine. I mean, she told them she was me -- she used my name. When the cops searched that name and saw the smiling face of a dykey-looking white girl with Illinois residency, the jig was up. The cops maybe called her mom, who maybe called our grandmother, who must have called my mom, who called me to let me know. Or else she was charged with something, which included her being charged with giving a false name, which made it so that her mom had to find out and tell my grandmother so my grandmother could tell my mom in case it ever showed up on my record by accident. Because otherwise how would anyone know, since her mom and my mom have no reason to speak except after Thanksgiving dinner if they're both there and because they're The Women and my grandmother's too old, they are charged with the dishes and so do them together, and I have not once offered to help, not wanting to participate in such blatant and offensive gendering even though I equally hate the idea of two women doing everyone's dishes, everyone being mostly men. This side of my family is overgrown with men. Tall, heavy men who interrupt you when you talk and share a largeness of cranium that I've inherited. I'll probably also inherit their jowls.

I had sex with my cousin and as I explored her body with mine, I apologized for getting everything before her, the Walkman, the CD player, the second Boyz II Men album. I had sex with my cousin and as I probed her cunt with my fingers, I told her I hate them all too, how they treat people, how they dismiss and disparage their own family. I had sex with my cousin and as I slid two fingers inside, I told her she can't hate me, I'm not like them, I can't be, I am not this person sitting silent and well dressed in a stuffy room making little to no effort to play with her kids. I had sex with my cousin and taking a moment from sucking her clit I told her hey, guess what, she is doing okay, she is doing just fine, her children are beautiful and so is she. I don't remember if she responded. I had sex with my cousin and as I shoved into her harder and fuller and faster and deeper until I lost all sense of my hand, I told her I'm sorry, I'm sorry, I'm sorry. Then I woke up.

Megan Milks is a PhD. Candidate at the University of Illinois at Chicago. Her work has been published in *Thirty Under Thirty*, *Wreckage of Reason*, and *Fist of the Spider Woman: Tales of Fear and Queer Desire*. Her work can also be found in *Western Humanities Review*, *Everyday Genius*, *Pocket Myths: The Odyssey*, and other journals. Her short story "Slug" was adapted for performance on Montreal-based CKUT's Audio Smut radio show; "Tomato Heart" was adapted for a performance piece at Amherst College. She co-edits *Mildred Pierce Magazine,* mildredpierce.wordpress.com, and is a regular contributor to montevidayo.com.

CANDLES

LINDSAY HUNTER

I AM IN THE CANDLE SHOPPE I CAN'T HELP IT

THE NEW AUTUMN LINE IS ORANGE NUTMEG AND IT IS AS CLOSE TO BARF AS THE BOTTOM OF A DIP CUP

I DIPPED ONCE RIDING IN THE CAB OF THE TRUCK OF MY ONE TRUE LOVE, HE WAS DRIVING HE WAS GETTING A HAND JOB FROM A PUERTO RICAN PUTA WE WERE GOING ABOUT FIFTEEN MILES AN HOUR NOT EVEN ENOUGH FOR THE WIND TO LIFT MY HAIR IN A POWERFUL FUCK YOU WAY

I HAD STOLEN THE DIP AND THE CUP AND NO ONE NOTICED

THERE WAS A WEB OF JIZZ ON THAT BITCH'S SKORT, I SAW IT WHEN WE STOPPED FOR CIGARETTES SHE STOOD IN THE MAGAZINES AISLE DOING NOTHING

THAT WAS A LONG TIME AGO

JULIAN IS THE MANAGER OF THE CANDLE SHOPPE HIS ASS IS LIKE TWO HALVES OF A BASKETBALL I HAVE TRIED MANY TIMES TO TOUCH IT

MY FAVORITE SCENT IS BEACH SANDLES, IT IS SALTY

MY SON CALLS IT BITCH SANDLES

MY SON IS FOURTEEN HE IS ALWAYS STANDING WITH A BOOK A TOWEL A HAT HIS FOLDED CLAMMY HANDS COVERING HIS CROTCH HE DOES NOT KNOW I KNOW AND IT IS BETTER THAT WAY

I READ THAT IN A PARENTING MAGAZINE

WHEN JULIAN DESCRIBES SOMETHING AS "EARTHY" I KNOW WHAT HE MEANS IS "SHITTY"

I HAVE NEVER KNOWN A MAN WHO HAS MORE THAN TWO SYLLABLES IN HIS NAME

I HAD A DREAM JULIAN WAS SHOWING ME A CANDLE THAT WAS CALLED "SUCK IT LIKE A STRAW"

ITS COMPANION SCENT WAS "LICK YOU LIKE AN ICE CREAM CONE"

I HAVE NEVER BEEN ATTRACTED TO A MAN OF A DIFFERENT CULTURE BUT THAT ASS I AM NOT MADE OF STONE

I AM FONDLING A CANDLE SET CALLED HERBACEOUS TWILIGHT, I WANT TO ASK JULIAN WHY IT'S NOT JUST CALLED OLD FORGOTTEN BONG BUT HE IS HELPING AN OLD MAN OBSESSED WITH THE SMELL OF LAUNDRY

I HAVE FOUND THAT THE CANDLES WITH THE PRETTIEST COLORS ARE ALWAYS THE FOULEST, I WOULD LIKE TO HAVE SOME GREEN CANDLES BUT THEY ARE ALL CUCUMBER MELON

CUCUMBER MELON SMELLS LIKE AFTERBIRTH

I BREATHE WITH MY MOUTH OPEN WHEN I'M IN THE CANDLE STORE

SOMETIMES I AM SITTING AT HOME WITH A CRAVING AND I CAN'T PUT MY FINGER ON IT AND THEN BLAMMO, I WILL REALIZE I AM CRAVING THE TASTE OF THE CANDLE STORE

IT HAS A TASTE, I'M NOT ON GLUE

I JUMPED THAT PUTA BEHIND THE P.E. TRAILER, SHE PULLED MY HAIR AND SCREAMED AND I PUNCHED A TOOTH INTO HER THROAT

I TRY NOT TO FEEL VICTORY THINKING OF THAT

IT IS DIFFICULT NOT TO

I GOT INTO THAT BOY'S TRUCK AND TOLD HIM WHERE TO DRIVE AND WHEN HE PULLED OVER I CLIMBED INTO HIS LAP, THE LOOK IN HIS EYES

I LOVE THINKING OF THAT LOOK

JULIAN IS ASSURING THE MAN THAT THE FRESH COTTON CANDLE SET SMELLS EXACTLY LIKE BOUNCE DRYER SHEETS ONCE LIT

I KNOW THIS IS NOT TRUE, I KNOW IT ACTUALLY SMELLS LIKE KOOL-AID BACKWASH

THE OLD MAN IS ASIAN, I CAN SEE THAT NOW, THERE DIDN'T USED TO BE BUT ONE ASIAN IN THIS COMMUNITY BACK IN THE DAY, THE HIGH SCHOOL ALGEBRA TEACHER, BUT NOW THEY ARE EVERYWHERE, I SMILE EXTRA BIG AT HIM TO LET HIM KNOW I AM COMFORTABLE WITH OUR MULTICULTURAL SOCIETY

AND I AM

COMFORTABLE WITH IT, I MEAN

THE OLD MAN IS TELLING JULIAN HE HAS THE ORANGE NUTMEG LINE IN HIS DOWNSTAIRS BATHROOM, I FEEL SYMPATHY FOR THE SWIRLING VOMITOUS TOMB HIS HOUSE MUST BE

THERE CAME A DAY WHEN I RAN OUT OF CLASS TO BARF UP AGAINST THE LOCKERS, THERE WAS A BABY FOR A WHILE BUT THEN IT WENT AWAY

THE LORD TAKETH, THANK GOD

THE TRUCK BABY IS HOW I CAME TO THINK OF IT

I NEVER TOLD THE BOY, BUT I WISHED I HAD TOLD HIM SO HE COULD THANK ME FOR NOT TELLING HIM

JULIAN HAS FINISHED WITH THE MAN, I SEE HIM FIDDLING WITH SOME PAPERS AT THE REGISTER, I KNOW HE IS HOPING I WILL LEAVE

I WANT TO TELL JULIAN THE BESTSELLING CHILDHOOD SUMMER CANDLE HE SOLD ME LAST WEEK SMELLS LIKE BUBBLE GUM WEDGED BETWEEN TWO FUNGUS TOES

SOMETIMES YOU KNOW WHEN YOU SHOULDN'T SAY SOMETHING

IF JULIAN WERE A CANDLE HE'D BE NAMED AMARETTO EXPLOSION OR MOCHA ANGEL

I WANT JULIAN TO BE A CANDLE

SO I CAN TAKE HIM HOME

IT IS FIVE MINUTES FROM CLOSING TIME, I DROVE HERE AFTER THERE WAS NOTHING ON TELEVISION AFTER MY SON ATE HIS DINNER IN HIS ROOM AFTER I PICKED UP THE PHONE AND PUT IT BACK DOWN AFTER I SAT ON MY PORCH TO WATCH THE SUN SET AFTER THE SUN MELTED LIKE THE DISCONTINUED PSYCHEDELIC SHERBET LINE

I DROVE HERE I CAN'T HELP IT

BEACH SANDLES SMELLS LIKE THE DIRT ROAD ME AND THE BOY PULLED OVER ON

I CAN'T HELP IT

I WAS A HOT BITCH IN MY DAY BUT NOW I AM SHAPED LIKE A CANDLE

Lindsay Hunter is a writer living in Chicago, where she co-hosts the Quickies! reading series. Her work has been published widely online and in print, and her first book, *Daddy's*, is out now on featherproof books.

A MAN'S MOUTH

DAN ALAMIA

A very small nation found itself lodged inside a man's mouth. They'd been dislocated from their homeland and inhaled during one of the man's many long-winded rants. Because he ate incessantly, stuffing everything he could touch into his mouth, and because he compulsively unleashed gusting winds of pronouncements, threats and hysterical pledges, the man noticed nothing new. The nation, meanwhile, was battered relentlessly. Night offered no relief. The man mumbled and monologued in the late hours and then snored in his sleep.

A very small parliamentary session convened during one snoring period to discuss actions. Barely heard over the roar, the Prime Minister proposed a message be sent to the man to initiate a new relationship of mutual benefit. Perhaps if the man gorged himself less and tested silence in deference to their nation, they could provide some service. Maybe they could each mind their own business. A puffed-up caucus of representatives objected to this as moot. They did not know the man's language, and in any case, such a proposal weakened the nation's sense of pride. Why must they make accommodations? Why did they not simply return to their homeland? The Prime Minister and a number of representatives dismissed the idea as utopian. How would the whole nation relocate, and furthermore, how would they ever make the journey to their original perch—or even find it?

Three citizens then spoke up, one clearly in the lead. They were among those who had lost family members in the daily sonic booms and avalanches of grease and gristle, animal, vegetable and mineral. The man would only understand the most direct warning, they said, a sharp attack on the softest, most vulnerable place they could find. There would be no ignoring that. There were some nods at this idea plus an isolated whoop from among the visitors in the public gallery. The head of state felt nervous. Violence destabilized order by definition, and furthermore, the man was capable of crushing their people. The Prime Minister was not suicidal. Hoping to avoid an accusation of weakness, he announced that the proposal would be, without delay, studied by a committee. In the mean time, an alliance could be formed as a transitional measure. This didn't seem to satisfy the three men, but the Prime Minister chose his moment. He corralled votes. Language would be gleaned from the man's guttural blasts and contact made.

A very small team deciphered the man's tongue. A national corps painted tall letters on a massive banner to spell out a simple message in accordance with the intelligence of the declarations and pledges barreling down on them. They coated the banner with a bitter oil to ensure the man did not eat it. The message, launched towards the tip of the man's tongue, read: *We are. Consider us.*

The man hacked and spat out the paper fiber. He examined it, pinched between his fingernails, and then brought it under a magnifying glass. A wave of fear swelled in him. He thought he was alone. He'd been invaded. Tears welled in his eyes. How dare they expect anything when it was they who were trespassing! He flicked the fiber to the floor and returned to his usual behavior—with more vigor.

The nation continued to suffer. Soon an emergency conference found the three men who advocated a sharp shock with a larger contingent. Now the pressure to act was greater. The Prime Minister called the men aside and authorized a mission, in exchange for their public support of his official plan, which was to prepare another massive banner. They agreed. Before the banner could be completed, the unofficial mission had launched three needle-like projectiles into a canker sore just below the gum line of one of the man's teeth.

The man cried out and clapped his hands over his mouth. A silence ensued that both terrified the very small nation and filled them with a sudden rising excitement. For the man, the pain increased. He staggered, disoriented, flailing, destroying his living room. He clawed his fingers into his mouth, drew blood, but couldn't feel his way to the source. He beat his fists against his head and cried. What had he ever done? Moral and hard-working his whole life! He fell to the ground and pressed dirt into his gums. Then he launched an assault of chemicals. Shampoo, cough syrup, rubbing alcohol. That was it for the very small nation.

Several days passed. The pain diminished. The man, however, fell ill. Silenced, weak in bed, he sipped broth. He was strong, he told himself. He could overcome anything. Still, even as he recovered, he was debilitated by the fear that a very small nation might take up inside him again. There was no way to know. Ceaseless inspection of his mouth provided no relief. What did that prove?

Weeks passed. His rants and bottomless appetite returned. And after more time had passed, he relaxed the fevered scouring of his gums and tongue and teeth. Only occasionally did he feel a ghost of a painful pang in his mouth which shamed him for the weakness it suggested.

Dan Alamia's work can be found in *Café Irreal*, *Yankee Pot Roast*, and *apt*, which is published by Aforementioned Productions. He has also been a contributing writer for NoveList. He lives near Philadelphia.

POEM WITHOUT MANNERS

KYLE MCCORD

Dear Nancy Drew, did you catch me earlier, gawking as you dredged
the bog for an ancient scepter? I slammed the book shut before I could see.
One could lose their grip riding trains in the outback. An aged pensioner nudges me awake
and makes some declaration about Gallipoli. A splotchy cosmos printed on the seats
reminds us that we are akin to astronauts, drinking in recycled air,
then artificial night. It hits each of us like a mysterious gas. How do you feel
about the German love affair with railways? Without the werewolf seductress, there is no "Europa"
no "Wolfenstein" without its pixilated, fascist inhabitants. If no Beatrice
then how will I ever escape hell? I face the fear that I might wander these continents
long after your hint of almond perfume fades from the page, after salt thrown over a shoulder
over a curse has settled.

Nancy, can I call you Tracy? Sweetheart? I was born an old Satchmo of a soul
and how long do you think we actually have to feel happy? One could lose their sense of scope
seeing so much of their twenties through protective glass. Ewes trot unsteadily along the meadow
which washes by like a plate. Late August coming on with its tuft tail and varicose leaves
shedding toward minimalism above where a sweet but slow-witted girl is walking. She glances up
from a poem where her life is over. Tracy, I want that to be something
you can solve: the mystery of the covetous father. A city is hopelessly lodged in the girl's eye,
and every branch which does not bear fruit surely burns, her father tells her
and returns to his paper. Every branch which burns also longed to blossom, she thinks.

CHILDHOOD WITH HYPNOPOMPIC OVERTURE

KYLE MCCORD

Our shared fear, friend, is that we were children abandoned on a boat
with one oar. You've rowed tirelessly on since before the invention of memory
but when I count backwards from ten, you will begin to pack away in an attic
the listless stares of those thick adolescents in stained camo overcoats
who couldn't conceive how you'd arrived here. Their eyes
like ruptured stars, sucking in everything in a wordless vacuum.
Nine, in a mythical brick fort with the radiators too close for code, and eight,
how many second-degree burns did you see? Seven, and hunter's education's
a required course no matter how much your father protests.
But this, six, slips out your ear onto the floor like army ants
in a cartoon. You reach into your pocket for a flask from which, five, you dump
that afternoon when Jared, who'd repeated tenth grade three times, pushed
the effeminate boy down some steps, cracked his ribs with steel-toed boots.
Four, and you'd have forgotten it all, painting miniatures in sanguine and cyan
in your parents' basement, three, if everything in the town weren't so tiny.
Miniature bakery, pocket-sized barbershop, and as you row on
into memory, the water swishes away their tiny prejudices and slights
that couldn't help become part of you, two, the way a landslide makes
shattered pillars and splintered doors features of a home. One, as it flows
with demonic speed from the hills with the snap of a finger: a weary
muscle which wakes you under clouds and the smell of dusted wood, a dock
wriggling beneath your back.

WELCOME TO UNEMPLOYMENT, MASSACHUSETTS

KYLE MCCORD

It's a modest limbo we inhabit: corn tacos on Tuesday, enough anytime minutes
and uninvolved evenings. The aimless souls besiege your house demanding to pick weeds
from your garden for change. Your mother allows it, while a woman you love is weeping
because the orchestras of the world sound worse for lack of funding.
The meals on credit and time, indeed, worse for being borrowed.
Eliot's Prufrock invites us to accept our role as the prom kings and queens
we were not. But, honestly, he was a sad, hard genius as so many of his era.
He didn't clip coupons or die face down in the Black Forest as others did
but in a show of humanity nearly lost his mind when his wife capitulated to insanity.
In this hive of inactivity, I drive through the darkened suburbs of Boston
where curtains thinly divide Monday from Tuesday, October from sailing season.
A fold of blurred strip malls. Says my Hebrew textbook: now you know the truth—
even heaven is only two waters. There are three things Satan would do anything
to take from you. Instruct me what they are.

Kyle McCord is the author of two books of poetry. *Galley of the Beloved in Torment* was the winner of the 2008 Orphic Prize. His second book is a co-written book of epistolary poems entitled *Informal Invitations to a Traveler* forthcoming from Gold Wake Press. He has work forthcoming or featured in *Boston Review*, *Columbia Poetry Journal*, *Cream City Review*, *Gulf Coast*, *Volt,* and elsewhere. He lives in Des Moines where he teaches and co-coordinates the Younger American Poets Reading Series and is an editor at *iO: A Journal of New American Poetry*.

MANNEQUIN

THEODORE WOROZBYT

The water had a white throat I stuck my fingers down once a morning. Out popped thirty poppy colored diamonds. The linen cloths lie folded behind the mirrored doors. Goodbye skeleton key, I said, though it was gone. The platinum stayed hidden in the cleaning solution for months and checks folded in skin bled invisible ink under the suitcase that packed itself every night when the music-box-bottomed Dresden steins and the cases tumbled and the sun vanished with the stones of the Coliseum and the clock of glass in the green world went smashing before the bitter spit of a lie's hated admission and I heard the shatter of blood in my heartways heartaways. I loam beets, and every blood colored thing I am left beating with I loathe. Some have rings all the way inside. Even the sun colored ones taste like candy lies, what with that propylus taste, the royal jelly. My toes need a mannequin, she said.

JUPITER

THEODORE WOROZBYT

The red storm shrinks but doesn't slow. "It had been there several, several weeks," the chief said by the river. I can still smell the garlic though I've eaten it, in a way. When we make our bid, the usufruct that anchors us is only another noise on the roof, or knuckles drummed on bread. Things move faster but the siren means to be mournful. The dead dog walks around in the live one. Everyone I know is angry about Pluto. Actually no, I don't know anyone angry about Pluto. A thump now and then outside the window sounds not quite outside. There's a fish in my ribs and an egg sliding there, cold on my tongue.

Theodore Worozbyt's work has recently appeared or is forthcoming in *Antioch Review*, *Crazyhorse*, *The Iowa Review*, *Po&sie*, *Shenandoah*, *The Southern Review*, *TriQuarterly Online,* and *Quarterly West*. He has published two books of poetry, *The Dauber Wings* (Dream Horse Press, 2006) and *Letters of Transit*, which won the 2007 Juniper Prize (The University of Massachusetts Press, 2008). He is an assistant professor of English at Georgia Perimeter College.

MEMORY/CITY

JOHN MORTARA

i hold in my hands a city

        a city filled with people
        very similar to people
        i have known

see:
      this one looks just like daniel
          all red sox hat and boston sweatshirt transplant
          all scraggly scruff fat-nosed
             his droned after-joint eeyore-esque groans

he might as well be daniel here in my city

and because it is my city i make it lean closer to the sun in the morning and fully bow to the moon in the
evening and the buildings
        (they too are mine)
             have trouble breathing just like me
               wheezing the wind down narrow
alleys where someone
     who looks just like sanchez
        widow's peak slightly chubby cheeks shiny lip ring and everything
          grins that relaxed mischief up and down his stocked frame and folds
        my college diploma
        into a giant paper airplane

        sails it away into the shadowy traffic of mass transit beasts
        farting themselves downstreet
          rolling past parking deck
            after parking deck
              each a hung swatch of
              blah beige

and of course i simply sigh and catch it with a pinch of my fingers
      take deep breaths / quietly clear the roads / repaint / etc

      (even my city runs away with me   sometimes)

but see how in this city
      there is a curly-blond-haired young lady
      that reminds me so much of millie
          not wild fits of party like i remember
          no longer go-to weekly mentor
          no more warm mother-chuckles over dinner

          instead now i see her
               slouched under the dry drone
               of the diner
               all black-shoe uniformed
               pinned-up smile bored sweaty

                    years spent trying to escape this city.

THINGS I HAVE LEARNED ABOUT HUMAN EXISTENCE WHILST BEING A ROBOT

JOHN MORTARA

01.   most surroundings are mostly uninteresting to most humans

michael told me no one knows the difference between
earth and dirt quite like he does standing on the sidewalk
corner of president and utica avenue asking questions

but michael is mostly uninteresting to most humans
{ he is unassuming in his asking } muttering and feverish
with queries and not one human asks why he asks what he asks

but i was never built to say "no" to new data like michael
so electrically available

02.   silence is almost never comfortable

judy has not told me anything and neither
margaret or robert or serena but i have observed
how all eight eyes turn to reservoirs of regret

so i probe { they are secretive in their hurt }
and run simulations of a brother's random relapse
that burned the brownstone unexplained

now that vague monster lingers beneath the christmas table
so ominously quiet

03.   humans spend a lot of time making sure others know what their bodies are called

alex told me he needs to make a mark of little ticks
and tacks on stone-faced earth { he is scientific in his art }
needs evidence of his Here but i see no him in it

though now i wander, looking for what his final tag
might be: a headstone, a book, framed flesh graffiti?
labels and labels and labels and labels and labels

i never knew files quite like these beings, disorganized
but so meticulously named

John Mortara lives, writes, and teaches in Wilmington, North Carolina, where he is also an MFA student at the University of North Carolina Wilmington. John is a co-creator and editor of *This Zine is a Spaceship*. His favorite color is purple.

BANGED BY AN ALIEN: A SHORT MEMOIR

AMY BUTCHER

It happened one night in January when it was cold, and there was snow on the sides of the road, and that snow had turned gray with itself, and everything else about this night was also perfectly predictable: the cardboard coasters with palm trees, the sap-colored beer, the conversation at the bar with the guy I liked about literary awareness, or flying squirrels I'd seen on Craigslist, or the STD iPhone app that you could pee on, or the escalating violence in Egypt, or all of the technology, all of it—the new phones, and the 3D theaters, and the holographic soccer players Japan had proposed, and were they real? Could they be real?

"No," we agreed. There was no way they could be real.

Everything was normal. Everything was the way it always was. And then, all of a sudden, there were aliens.

But before the aliens, there was this: a bar tab, which I paid, and then I took my cream-colored pea coat—the one that with my fair skin and blond hair makes me look like a hulking tator tot—and I said to the guy at the bar, "Well, I'm off to pick up those squirrels," even though I wasn't, even though what I really planned to do was go home and watch *Teen Mom 2*. The ad on Craigslist said the squirrels would be in a cage by the side of the road. They were free to the first person who showed. I felt bad for them, out there in the cold, but what was I going to do about it?

"That would be great," the guy said. "Then if I came over, I could sit on the couch, and they would jump from wall to wall. That would be crazy."

"Sure," I said, "except not jump. *Fly.*"

He laughed and stayed put. Of course he didn't come with me. So I crossed the street, and at the convenience store bought a Laffy Taffy—red, because that's the kind that comes with sprinkles—and then I headed for home. It was the sort of night where the wind pushing through the trees makes you think about your life, when the open spaces between the branches make you think you should be doing more with it. I put my headphones on. I listened to Bruce Springsteen's 'You're Missing,' thinking, *Everything* is *everything*, and thinking this was deep. When I looked up, there they were.

There were six of them in all. They were playing hopscotch on a grid done in coral sidewalk chalk, three on the board and three off it, waiting their turn. Their skin was the color of khaki. It was loose. They looked smooth, like polished stone, like if you touched them, you'd want to go on touching. You'd want to rub your thumb over their edges and revel in their smoothness. But when they moved—throwing a stone and edging their bodies forward—

their skin rippled with movement. It was wet. It was the way Jell-O looks when you pull it from the fridge too early and the gelatin hasn't set. How some parts stay stationary, and some parts do not, and it's the inside that carries the wave. Their skin wobbled like that, contained.

"Hi," I said. I didn't know what else to say. I didn't want to be rude. I pulled the edges of my coat tight around my frame.

"Hi," they said. They said it in unison, as if they sensed things on cue. Their voices were all the same, their language, perfectly understandable. It wasn't English; it sounded nothing like what we speak. But I could understand it. It surprised me how I'd carried this ability all along, how I'd carried it without even knowing. I wondered what else I could do, the things I was capable of, if only I tried.

I dragged my toe along the grid of their board. "This is pretty," I said. "I admire your use of pastels."

"Thanks," they said. The smallest of them picked up a brick of red chalk, the edges rubbed to sharp peaks. He set to work drawing a gumball dispenser, filling the space with small pocks of color. Another drew a tornado, the rigid lines blue and thick where he pressed.

"Are you…?" I asked.

"Aliens," one said. He took a step forward.

This one was big, his body tall and round. I raised my hand and placed it firmly on his shoulder. Ripples formed and washed down his torso. They moved and kept moving, long after I touched him.

"I just had to see," I said.

My reaction to him was the same as nearly everyone. The fantasies almost never introduce themselves at first. Normally, I meet a man and I think, *This could be okay.* I don't like him very much but I give him a shot. We go for pancakes and he asks the waitress for more cream for the coffee when he realizes there is only one small white pouch left and it's polite to let me have it. Later, he texts me about the pancakes and how they made him feel sick, or how they made him feel great, or sometimes how it was not the pancakes he liked at all but sitting there next to me. This is how it begins. Then we see a movie at two o'clock on a Tuesday or he stops by to tell me that my drain is not broken at all but simply needs Drain-O. He walks me to the hardware store and helps pick out the right bottle.

That is when it all changes. I stand in my bathroom barefoot as he pours the liquid into my tub. He says, "There you go," and I think that maybe now I love him. I give in pretty easy then. I begin to fix him dinner. I let him talk to me about "trips." At night, when he leaves, I think about the future. The fantasies begin to take shape: first a porch with splintered cornflower blue floorboards, then the dog everyone thinks is stupid. He has a strange overbite, but that is misleading. He is impressively bright. We name him after our favorite snack. Triscuit, maybe, or Skittles.

The fantasies always develop slowly except with the guy at the bar. He was the only one that made them come quick. I saw him and thought, *Backyard creek where we catch crawfish and drink beer.* I thought, *We name them all Lobster and put them in a fishbowl on our counter.*

"You're pretty," the alien said. He took a step closer. I felt him warm, the heat escaping his edges.

"Thank you," I said.

The wind picked up and we stood there quietly, listening to it wash down the hillside and over the valley. We could hear branches bending, hear the trees as they gave.

"I like you," the alien said.

I wasn't sure I liked him, but I did feel happy. I couldn't tell if it was leftover from earlier or some new thing. It was likely the former—at the bar, the guy had touched my shoulder, saying, "I *told you* so," and kept it there long enough for me to think, *Beat-up red barn, goats for pets*—but I decided to try and pretend. There was nothing to lose. It was nice to be standing there, to be able to look at the alien and keep on looking, unafraid of what he might make of it.

"I like you, too," I said.

He took my hand in his—a long, pliable tube I could feel between each finger. "Come with us," he said. In the brick courtyard just beyond the sidewalk, a whirling green orb pulsed and spun.

"A portal?" I asked.

"Of course," he said.

Once, I was in the backseat of a friend's car, and she was playing 'Burning Down The House.' Her boyfriend was in the front seat, and when the light went red he turned around and asked me, "If an alien came down right now and asked you to go with him—he would take you back to his planet, and he would show you everything—but you couldn't come back to tell anyone what you saw, would you go?" And I didn't even have to think twice about it. I said, "Yeah, I would go," because of course if given the chance I would elect to fly through space, or sit shotgun in a spaceship, or press my warm forehead against the cool, cold glass, watching the clouds pull apart, watching the land masses come together in shapes I knew, saying first, "There's Italy," and then, "There's Africa."

I told the guy in the front seat that I wanted to know if aliens ate supper and what they did with their time.

"Is there alien Shake-And-Bake?" I asked. "Can aliens read?"

I told him I wanted to know if aliens had pets, if they kept them on leashes. Was their world split and sold as real estate? Was there such a thing as private property? Maybe aliens had communal living, I argued, where everything was both theirs and everyone's. Or maybe they owned entire mini-universes, where they controlled the climate with remotes full of colorful buttons.

I said, "Of course I would go," but of course there was another reason. It was one that was so clichéd and simplistic that even in that backseat I could never admit it. But it was the most pressing truth, clichéd or not, and that's what it kept coming back to. How it seemed worth it to take my chances. I wasn't certain life on Earth would ever get any less stupid. Each morning, I woke up, made four cups of coffee, wrote a paragraph, bought some home décor item—curtains or a shag rug or salt and pepper shakers shaped like canaries—and then I reread the paragraph, revised a sentence or two, and deleted the rest. I walked into town where I bussed tables at a restaurant named after a sea animal. Then I walked home. That was it. That was my every day.

There was possibility for excitement, sure, but I only ever saw it in men. The one from the bar especially. Each night, after my paragraph and throw pillows and god-knows-what he did with his days, we met up at a bar that smelled like a woodshed. We sat at a table held together with tape. He liked me, maybe, or else he didn't but was good at making it seem that way. We'd drink round after round, and sometimes his leg and my leg would bump under that crappy wooden table, but we'd both pretend it didn't happen. We'd move our legs away in a sort of quick shuffle. One of us would say, "Man, I love this song," to avert the attention, or else, "Another round? This one's on me."

We'd sit like that for hours. He would talk, and I would sit there and think about all the things we could do if only we talked about what we had. There were so many things we could do if only we talked about *what we had*. I don't mean intimacy. It had nothing in the world to do with sex. What I wanted was his closeness. What I wanted were his words. Outside, the cars coursed through our wet city and I sat wishing we could be like them. We could leave the bar and drive south until we reached Missouri. He could pump the gas and lean against the hood, brooding or else mysterious, and I could go inside to buy gum and sunflower seeds from a small pastel packet. The radio would play his favorite song, and he'd lean over against me, his shirtsleeve stiff from drying on the line. He'd say, "I danced to this when I was *a kid*," and I'd say, "Turn it up louder, *louder*!" We'd pluck the seeds from their pouch, hold them between our teeth and then spit them out into the dark, dry night, Missouri's black heat rushing in from between our downed windows. "You think they'll grow?" he'd ask, and I'd say, "Hope so." I'd like the idea of a marker: a way to indicate we had been some place in the world together.

Or else maybe it would be something different, something closer. Maybe we would climb onto our bikes and ride the two miles of flattened road north, crossing the highway overpass and stopping at the apex to look below, the few white and red dots the only lights for miles. Later, at the lake, we'd ditch our bikes at the metal guardrail and then sneak down the hillside. We'd peel off our shirts and jeans not out of want but necessity. I'd splash into the inky water, a pocket of moon casting wet light, and he'd wiggle his arms as they moved through the undercurrent. "I'mma snake," he'd say, grabbing hold of my ankle. "Ssss-sss, ssss-ss."

But of course we never talked about that—who talks about feelings? We just talked about miniature ponies and syntax. Once, when it was late and we were still in the bar, I said, not knowing how else to say it, "You know— you've got to know how I feel about you."

"Sure," he said, poking a toothpick through his teeth. "I feel, you know, I feel that way too." Then he shook his head. "But I don't think any of that is too smart."

He said it so simply, so matter-of-fact. I trusted his wisdom, how it could be better than mine. I didn't bring it up again. And so each night we'd drink, and I'd sit there quietly thinking, *Maybe now we will talk, maybe* now, *maybe* now. But of course we never did. And at the end of the night, I was always alone.

The thought of an alien planet and an alien boyfriend was exciting. Maybe he could spin himself invisible, or change his color or consistency, or travel under the ocean by designing a series of intricate tunnels with his mind. Maybe he could mold lava into glass art, or grow flowers along his forehead, or pause lightning bolts long enough for us to step inside them. Maybe he could build a birdfeeder—a yellow one with blue shutters and a white door— and I could hang it up and stand there beside him. We could admire and name every bird that flew in.

"I wouldn't go," the guy in the front seat said, "because I think so much of going is about coming back to report."

And it seemed to me, in that backseat, that that was what a lot of life was about. Not so much doing something, but being able to later say you did it. To claim that you went to a place, or you conquered a thing, or you saved squirrels that can fly in a cage by the side of the road not because you did, but because of what it said about you when you said it. The speaking is what's most important.

I went with the alien. He held me to his chest and we rose above the icy stratosphere. I felt his heart beat, the pumping he willed the organ to have. Later, he led me down his alien corridor and through his alien apartment lobby, and I touched all of the metal, the shining and glittering metal. In his floating bed we banged, his sounds swirling around us in the darkness.

"Is this okay?" he'd ask, and I couldn't see why it wouldn't be. We did everything. We made all kinds of noise.

It's over for me on Earth now and I can't say that I am sorry. The planet spins in the inky distance and it doesn't matter I won't come back. It's not the miles but the time that can make a person quiet. You lose that sense of urgency and you lose your sense to feel. We finish and roll over, and my alien presses me to his torso. We say things into the darkness and he squeezes me through outer space. I squeeze back and hold him close and put into drawers those things once worth saying. You wouldn't believe how well it works. You wouldn't believe how good it feels.

Amy Butcher is a current graduate student of the Nonfiction Writing Program at the University of Iowa. Her work has appeared or is forthcoming from the *Indiana Review*, *Michigan Quarterly Review*, *Brevity*, *Upstreet*, *Hobart,* and *PANK*.

SEXY

ALISHA KARABINUS

In the first days of the first house, our Little Rock house, I warned you: *I'm nosy, so nosy; I will read the browser history and the tags in your clothing and anything you leave lying around,* so when your flash drive was there, glinting like the last piece of candy, I opened it up and gobbled the contents. I chewed it all, the round-ass porn and the notes from short stories you lost interest in, brain scraps like keys to doors I'd never even seen. But sometimes those doors open to pit-traps and I know this, I played all those games, I knew to test the floor, to leave some stones unturned, but **PAM LETTER** was too good, too much, and my clicking finger was clicking before my own brain scraps could scrape together and say, hey, *no.*

And then on the screen, that fear, uncurling: maybe I wasn't the *only* one for you, or even the *best*, or even the one you wanted to fuck against a chain link fence. Words leapt off the LCD and clawed my eyes. *ROSE* was a thorn in my chest, because it came from a poem that was ours, from the first poem I read so long ago while sitting with you in the dry Oklahoma grass, from the first book I brought into our home. I am your rose, not this woman, older now in my head, dried up, horrible, unappreciative, clearly in need of a good murdering—not a rose, but something dead and sagging. *LOVE* broke my heart and kicked my teeth down my throat, though I knew it, though you told me—you spilled it all, in halting phrases, when I dragged the words out of your mouth over Memphis beers.

But *SEXY* is the one that sticks, the one I remember now, months later, after that day, when I fell on your sleeping body with my fists, when I screamed my anger, when you had to hold my arms for a moment before you crept away, head down, waiting to see if I would begin throwing clothes back into the boxes they'd so recently spilled from, but I didn't, I relaxed, I let go, I held you, I loved you hard and painful, ripped my name into your shoulders, and when we went to Waffle House and laughed over the everything in your hashbrowns, I know you thought I forgot, or tamped it all down, enough for us to go on, to share this space, these bodies, this air, but—

SEXY always creeps back, even when our hands are wrapped together in knots, even when we're kissing and kissing, even when I've forgotten which tongue is mine and which is yours, I see it, thin font, heavy words: *You're so sexy when you mow the lawn in your old t-shirts.* Such a simple detail, it sticks, setting up camp deep in the curls of my brain. I wiggle my hips when I wash the dishes; I wear t-shirts, dresses, nothing, everything to steal that word for myself, but I find only silence when I look for it in your mouth.

Alisha Karabinus is a founder and managing editor of *Revolution House* magazine and is set to begin an MFA adventure in Fiction at Purdue University. Her work has appeared or is forthcoming in such publications as *Per Contra*, *Staccato*, and *Flashquake*. She dislikes most cheese, stray hair, and slow traffic on fast roads.

CLOSE

ANDREW ROE

An older man and a younger man (father and son perhaps), the latter mentioning a woman with a kid and prescriptions for multiple medications, the former then offering some relationship advice, saying, "Don't get too close," the latter then nodding and agreeing and saying, "I know, I know. I'll try. I won't."

Andrew Roe's fiction has appeared in *Tin House*, *One Story*, *The Sun*, *Glimmer Train*, *The Cincinnati Review,* and elsewhere. His reviews and non-fiction have appeared in *The New York Times*, *San Francisco Chronicle* and Salon.com. He lives in Oceanside, California, and keeps a sporadic blog at andrewroe.blogspot.com.

MUCHACHAS ENVEJECIENDO

BY ÉDGAR RINCÓN LUNA

Las he visto
hermosas
con lágrimas dibujar el adiós en sus rostros
amables
amables labios pronunciando palabras oscuras
he visto sus cuerpos
inmóviles sombras del beso
                                        eclipsadas
por un cuerpo más rosa y más dispuesto
                        más animal mordiendo el día
                        y a la noche

mientras el sol de sus cuerpos está alejándose
la luz de sus cinturas adolescentes
                                        envejece

Édgar Rincón Luna was born in Ciudad Juárez, Mexico in 1974. He is the author of *Aquí comienza la noche interminable* (2000) and *Puño de whiskey* (2005).

GIRLS GROWING OLD

TRANSLATED BY TOSHIYA KAMEI

I've seen
beautiful girls
with tears drawing goodbye over their faces
friendly girls
friendly lips saying dark words
I've seen their bodies
still shadows of the kiss
                          eclipsed
by a body pinker and readier
        like an animal biting day
        and night

while the sun of their bodies is moving away
the light of their adolescent waists
                      grows old

Toshiya Kamei is the translator of Liliana Blum's *The Curse of Eve and Other Stories* (2008), Naoko Awa's *The Fox's Window and Other Stories* (2010), and Leticia Luna's *Wounded Days and Other Poems* (2010).

DEAR GENDER IDENTITY

BRENT GOODMAN

Thank you for the larger-than-average penis.
That helps kickstand my confidence unzipped
elbows akimbo at the middle urinal. Thank you
for the Yoni too, sacred whirlpool always longing
to guide other men's bodies inside mine. Ask me,
the whole garden is goddamn delicious.
Between lives all the Barbie and Ken dolls
exchange expressions. *What are the pluses
of a bulge here vs. two there?* they compare.
Ascend or descend? Inny or outy?
My soulmate's sister prefers kissing girls.
One of his brothers craves boys so much
now s/he's a born-again post-op princess.
Best I've reassembled was a water balloon bra
when I was twelve. Thank you for the honest bent
I guess. It helps bond broader orbits, the subtle
ache of any sphere gracing gravity's passing influence.
The warmest summer afternoon I can remember was
seeing the neighbor's toddler son in the front yard
whirling in circles wearing nothing but his older sister's sundress
while both parents smiled, clapped, and sang. Thank you,
beloved friends of the universal uncommon. Thank you
for the choice between the body people see and
this fountain pouring your blinding spirit into mine.

DEAR HISTORY

BRENT GOODMAN

Mayflies lack mouths but mate on the wing.
There was a period dirigibles once purred
above great cities and coupled with skyscrapers.
Uncle Oddball, who collects petrified lightning
anymore? *Fulgurite*, he writes on tiny placards
each time the windows thunder. Mayfly swarms
mistaken for mist at sunrise. Branching relics
sing in tissue paper gift boxes like crystal chimes.
A waitress serving steaming coffee to day traders
atop a rooftop garden cafe catches the smile of a
passing airship pilot. Her hairdo so 1922. The sky
carries their feet and for a moment together they rise.

Brent Goodman is the author of *The Brother Swimming Beneath Me* (2009) and *Far From Sudden* (forthcoming 2012), both from Black Lawrence Press. His work has appeared in *Diode*, *Poetry*, *Zone 3*, *No Tell Motel*, *Barn Owl Review*, and elsewhere. He lives and works in Rhinelander, Wisconsin. He is online at www.brentgoodman.info.

RAPTURE

OCEAN VUONG

We are holding hands at the edge
of a rooftop. Below—a city
we have yet to conquer
and therefore, will not miss.

In the distance, water,
and beyond that, a new sun.
At first it is small, a ruby

lifted by the waves' diaphanous gesture.
Slowly it swells, it blooms
until the sky is nothing
but concentric spheres of fire.

Its surface ravaged with red seas
shifting in lesions of incalculable heat.
Flames so close, steam is rising
from our cheeks.

I know I am dreaming, love.
But if for nothing else,
I would step into that raging star
smiling, as though to enter
the impossible arms
of the god I refused, but knew
by name.

Do not wake me. Let me go.
For I can never love you
like fire, the way it clings
to skin against the wind.
The way it burns to know
the secret taste of marrow.

HOLES

OCEAN VUONG

Let us take what is given
more slowly, as if created incomplete—a hole
unfilled, a mouth gasping for air, salt.

Impossible to keep the flesh
which enters, suffices;
the warmth, not our own

but makes us whole nonetheless.
And if the body is a leaking vessel,
let us suck a little harder,

lick clean the dew percolating
in the wired hairs of our sex—
tongues suspended in supplication.

Desire is never self-conscious
and perhaps, it's for the better: the boy
lying face-down in his living room

waiting for strangers to come like mercy,
plow him out of that wretched sack of bones
into something evanescent: a cry of joy,

a stain, a shadow wilting on the wall.
And if to be touched is to be lovely,
what else but to seek or be sought?

After all, the boy will unravel eventually
into darkness, where sleep comes
through the slow erosion of hours.

Where he fades alone into the shade
of a room with its light turned out
and his body, with all its gaping holes

whispering
          more
    more

                    more

Born in Saigon, Vietnam, Ocean Vuong is the author of the chapbook BURNINGS (Sibling Rivalry Press, 2010) and is currently an undergraduate at Brooklyn College, CUNY. His was a semi-finalist for the 2011 Crab Orchard Series First Book Award and has received an Academy of American Poets award, the Connecticut Poetry Society's Al Savard Award, as well as four Pushcart Prize nominations. Poems appear in *RHINO*, *diode*, *Lantern Review*, *Softblow*, *Crate*, and *Union Station*, among others. Work has also been translated into Hindi, Korean, Vietnamese, and Russian. He lives in Brooklyn and is an avid supporter of animal rights and veganism. He is online at www.oceanvuong.blogspot.com.

HOW TO HAVE AN AFFAIR

HEATHER FOSTER

I. Say no (meaning yes).

Hot, hard breath from your
nose, all cloves
and black licorice,
your mouth
full of my
neck like a gag.
You were warmth
in my chest, like an infant
feeding, that burst
of oxytocin,
delirium of being
someone's sustenance.

II. Do it outdoors.

I was hoe-handle
deep in dirt—
wet black, rainspat,
flat on my back—
I dug out easy,
flipped over,
took my turn,
licked the grit
off my lip—
copper-chlorine, taste
for iron, taste for salt.

III. Use food.

It was autumn
in starlight on the tufted

velvet sofa.
Still naked, faces
still pink as French
radishes, you showed me
how to hold a fig
between three fingers,
softly, and raise it
to be bitten.
A thousand tiny
seeds to swallow.
We were almost normal.

IV. You're a monster. Act like it.

I thought I'd miss the taste
of the one
I loved before you—
his head, cattail-smooth,
smell of buttered corn.
But you've got me,
knees in the dirt, dew
on the hawthorn.
Whatever kernel of him
I craved is out of mind.
I'd rather be your
dirty girl, your fig eater.
Bury me again, tender
reaper, kill the old
me. Dig up a girl
with a taste for blood—
wax cross in my fist,
lemon in my mouth.

A former pre-med lab rat, Heather Foster shed the goggles and sold her soul to poetry. She now lives on a 144-acre farm in Tennessee with her husband, kids, and Ozzy the heavy metal rooster. She's an MFA candidate in poetry at Murray State University.

INTO THE HOUSE OF TRIUMPH
for Elise W.

REBECCA HAZELTON

Whenever I try
    to talk about the past, it becomes a jaguar throw
                    wrapped around
          your bare shoulders,
illegal plush, musky repulse,
while you, imperious and resolute, smoke
        from a cigarette holder—
    dahling, stop your whining.

          Jukebox jewel, princess cut,
    you were a libretto sung into the smut
        of The Claremont Lounge,
a bit of shining glass
        wedged between pleather cushions—

Meth gave you cheekbones to die for, whipped
    away the alcoholic plump, and
        burnished you
to a brief golden glamour—

    you posed in black and white
        with your breasts billowing to the camera,
    lips parted, Marilyning with the best of them,

    O, I have all the time now
          to listen
to your proclamations,
        and you have all the time to make them—
if there is one last story you'd like
        to star in, to shine again
          like a tinfoil tiara

just say, and I'll write you a final triumph
over friends like me, who disappeared
into smug sobriety, the snug safety
of a circadian life—

I hear you were still
an unapologetic blonde, *dahling,*
I hear your final word was *no.*

Rebecca Hazelton attended The University of Notre Dame for her MFA in poetry, and completed her PhD at Florida State University. She was awarded a fellowship year as the Jay C. and Ruth Hall Poetry Fellow at the University of Wisconsin-Madison Creative Writing Institute, and also received a fellowship from Vermont Studio Center. She teaches creative writing at Beloit College. D.A. Powell chose her poem "Book of Janus" for inclusion in Best New Poets 2011.

I TALK TO NUMBER 53 ABOUT NUMBER 9 AND OTHERS

MERRITT TIERCE

Those are pictures I gave to Owen and then took back.

When I was married I lived across the street from Owen, who lived with his sister in a low dark house on the corner lot. I would see him mowing, coming, going. He was bald and had a loping slow gait. I would see the father of the sister's child stopping by now and then in his sporty import, which in that neighborhood of Oldsmobiles and pickups was flashy. The sister talked compulsively and would speak to me if we were outside our houses at the same time. She was pudgy and wore hippie clothes, flowing patchwork skirts and blouses with strings. She had skin that was permanently pink and a nose with large nostrils, one of which was pierced, and flat thin oily dark hair and a sweet smile. She told me, even though I thought of myself as a stranger to her at the time, that she was frustrated by Aaron's purchase of the cool new black Volkswagen GTI when she and the baby had no money. Also he had satellite radio installed on it which she judged completely out of line.

Eventually I bought the same car for myself, although I bought the sedan version and Aaron had the coupe. This was my concession to parenthood. I shouldn't have spent so much money on a car either but at least my kids could open their own doors, whereas getting into the GTI would someday involve undignified folding and crouching for the young child of Aaron and Owen's sister.

I never spoke to Owen while I was married living across the street from him, and then we moved from the house into an apartment to save money. But the rent was only $160 less and after the deposit and the U-Haul I calculated the move was hardly worth it. Frequently we made incremental shifts like that, that availed nothing.

I handled the divorce myself. I was only twenty-two. I found some boilerplate documents and copied them, and created a tidy affidavit asserting I couldn't pay court costs. The aide who initially reviewed the paperwork told me I had left out some crucial piece but was unforthcoming about how to correct things. I went to the bathroom and cried and then went upstairs to the legal library they had and figured it out while my husband waited downstairs. I included no provision for child support, counting on continuing friendship between me and my intended ex-husband, which as you know has worked out so far. But meanwhile Owen's sister was embroiled constantly in some legal hassle or other, attempting to force Aaron to provide for her instead of buying things like new rims.

I had never been over to the low corner house while we lived across the street—my conversations with her had taken place in our driveways. But right before we moved she told me about a Montessori school in the country so I took the kids out of the church daycare they were in after there was a bulletin board of penguins in the foyer, a penguin with each child's name on it, with the crepe announcement that BIRDS OF A FEATHER FLOCK

TOGETHER FOR JESUS. I don't know what bothers me most about it, I said to my ex-husband, the cliché or the encouragement toward cultishness or the weird way they added 'for Jesus' at the end. Like you add 'in bed' to a fortune cookie fortune.

At the Montessori school, which was located in the farmhouse of the owner/teacher, even the smallest children helped prepare a hot lunch and were expected to assist in cleaning out the chicken coop. After the kids started going there Owen's sister invited me to bring them over to play with her baby daughter, which is how I met Owen.

Back then everything needed to happen immediately, I felt. That is how we stayed up all night the first time we hung out by ourselves, and how I forced him to have sex with me as dawn broke, even though he resisted. I did the same thing to my ex-husband, before he was my husband. He was helping me move into a new apartment in college and we hadn't even put the mattress up on the bedframe yet but I got on top of him and took him. He lost his erection after I got him inside me.

A similar inscrutable haste is why one morning I was in such a hurry to meet Owen for breakfast before I had to be at work. I dropped the kids off at the Montessori school but I left the door to the school open on accident and when I noticed it I thought I should get out and shut it but I didn't want to take four seconds to do that. To my thinking those might be the four seconds in which my boss would go from not noticing my lateness to getting irritated since she had to make the transition in some moment.

As I was driving away I wondered if the calm teacher would feel silently aggravated by my not shutting the door and would think I was more interested in getting off to my day than in giving my children a good beginning. That I was not one of those mothers who has so much patience they walk deliberately, peacefully out the door in the hall and take the time to shut it quietly as they step over the threshold and place a certain foot in the gravel.

My son would cry each morning when I left. Sometimes I would tell him he could wave at me out the window if he wanted to, and I would yell I love you from the car and blow him a kiss and wave back but I didn't offer him that the day I didn't shut the door. I drove too fast on the country road with sun in my eyes and met Owen at the breakfast place with ten minutes to give him. He was a tall man who ate like a cat, methodically, thoughtfully cleaning his fingers with his tongue and taking precise bites that spilled no juices. No crumbs fell, his long left leg crossed over his long right leg like a tail over paws. He had the same sweet smile as his sister, and a young, angular face. I'd seen pictures of him when he had hair, which was beautiful straight blond hair he wore long, it fell across one eye. He looked impenetrably handsome, like a punk star or somebody's famous friend. After I saw the hair pictures he seemed so vulnerable in his baldness.

He owned a tobacco shop in a strip mall, which is how he came to be known as Cigar Man to a later consort—that's you, you who are intrigued by all of my previous liaisons and to whom I am undoubtedly telling too much. Cigar Man, or Owen, had some software he used to track sales, but it was fairly primitive code and he did not know how to manipulate it in order to produce a certain needed report. I said I would look at it. I knew nothing about software myself but consulted my first boyfriend, with whom I was still in contact over email even though before I met Owen he had sort of raped me. What happened was his software company had temporarily stationed him in my town for a project and he got in touch with me, five years after I had thrown a small container of yogurt at his head the last time I saw him. So we were occasionally going to see movies at this arthouse theatre and I got a bit drunk at dinner and woke up at three in the morning and he was fucking me. I made a note of this somewhere. I went back to the note, which was dated, a year later because I ran into his mother in a Starbucks on the anniversary of the sort of rape, a coincidence I am unable to interpret. Someone had just hit her car in the parking lot so even though I hadn't seen her in so long she was distracted.

The first boyfriend solved the software problem and Owen was pleased with me and said at breakfast the next day when I asked if I could have another waffle Baby you can have whatever you want. What I wanted was to have sex every day. Owen was thirty-six, thirteen years older than me, but he had lost his virginity only three months before we met to a beautiful voluptuous blonde named Jeannie who told him she felt like she could be herself with him but went back to her boyfriend after awhile. When she quit him Owen smoked an entire pack of Marlboros in the bathroom and threw up. The Marlboros were punitive because as a tobacco store owner of course he smoked fastidiously handrolled drum tobacco.

I quit him too after one season, by cheating on him with a man whose middle name was Toussaint. He had been a counselor at a residential math camp for high achievers I went to the summer I was fourteen, and he'd invited me into his dorm room to give me a foot massage. At the time he was the coach of the university's club tae kwan do team and put a mattress on the floor to show me some moves. He did a body throw that knocked my breath out. He then did something else that I don't recall clearly.

I was working part-time at Barnes & Noble while I was seeing Owen, and one day the man whose middle name was Toussaint came into the store. I had not seen him in nine years. It was the year of bad reunions. He came over to my house that afternoon, and while the kids were in their cribs napping we sat in the living room. He asked me what my vices were. He said he had missed me so much. That turned me off because I hadn't even thought of him and there had been nothing between us except the foot massage and the body throw. Perhaps he thought I needed to hear that to be inclined to have sex with him, when I thought it was obvious I wanted to have sex since I invited him over.

He couldn't get hard though so I asked him to leave. It seemed lame that that should count as cheating on Owen, but I didn't care so much because I was tired of Owen and didn't know how else to end it. One night a couple of weeks before that Owen had been over at the apartment, in which I now lived alone with the kids, and I had stepped out to walk over to the complex's mail center. On the way back I passed some men drinking beer on a patio. They offered me a beer. I took one and stood there drinking it and not saying anything while they talked, until Owen came down the sidewalk and grabbed my arm and pulled me back to the apartment. He yelled at me, in his quiet cat way, and I went into a closet with a box cutter and cut my right biceps, or rather scored it as one does a vegetable before boiling it to remove the skin. The moment when he grabbed my arm had been surprisingly thrilling since I considered myself a smart woman and I didn't realize until then that a man would be rough with a smart woman. Afterwards this seemed like evidence that I wasn't so smart.

But while it was good we took a motorcycle trip out to the lake late at night. He had a Suzuki sport bike on which I could have lost my life, because he drove 118 miles per hour on that trip and the helmet he had for me was way too big. I couldn't tighten the chin strap enough to fix it so over the bridge the wind caught it and blew it off the back of my head. It was choking me because the wind was pulling it so hard but Owen was going so fast I was afraid to use one hand to loosen it. I was angry at him like a wild animal as that was happening but once we were over the bridge and once he slowed down I was happy I hadn't died and didn't say anything about it.

We took some good cheese and crackers and some chocolate out to the lake, which was in a state park that had closed hours before we arrived. We were going to take some weed too but at the last minute he said he didn't want to and we would smoke when we got back. We ate the cheese on some rocks at a deep part of the lake, looking at the stars. We took off our clothes and swam, and the park rangers found us. Two of them with flashlights—they came out on the rocks and asked us if that was our bike up on the hill and told us we were in violation because the park was closed and we had to get out of the water. One of them knelt and searched our backpacks, saying You don't have anything in here you shouldn't do you. No sir, said Owen, just the cheese and some chocolate there. The ranger said You know there's ants all over the cheese. We were treading water, and since I was naked I was trying to tread without coming out of the water too much. Owen said No sir I didn't know that. The other ranger was tougher and told me I had to get out. Owen said Sir could you please just let us get out after you leave and we'll go home.

I found out why he had not lost his virginity until he was thirty-six one morning when I asked if I could trim his bush. It was a pleasant ginger-colored soft bush but far overgrown. When was the last time you trimmed this, I asked. Well—never, he said. I laughed and laughed at this but not to be mean. I almost said Jeannie didn't ever say anything? but I stopped because I knew not to mention Jeannie. Instead I said Why did you wait so long to do it with a girl?

He said it was because of the fact that when he was twelve and his sister was six he bothered her. That was how he said it. We could hear his sister in the kitchen feeding the little one and talking on the phone to one of her friends about how Aaron had flaked out on his weekend with the baby, saying he was sick, but had been seen in a bar with this new bitch. Later I gave Owen some tasteful pictures of myself in shadowy poses. He put them away in a drawer so I took them back. Those are the pictures you found in the shoe box with the video. The video is from the surveillance camera at the cigar shop, we did it on the desk in the back room where he counted the money. Yes, I used to wear dresses.

Merritt Tierce is the executive director of the Texas Equal Access Fund and a graduate of the Iowa Writers' Workshop. She received a 2011 Rona Jaffe Foundation Writers' Award and lives in Denton, Texas, with her children.

MOTHER AND CHILD DIPTYCH

JOE WILKINS

Now that she is alone,
she walks to the river each evening

and throws in four stones.
She doesn't know why.

Some days they are for her children,
some days her husband. But today,

they are for that boy
she barely knew but kissed anyway
under the bleachers one recess.

***

He stares at his soggy Cheerios.
He would rather pancakes, a hard fried egg,
chokecherry syrup.

But his mother is still in her slip,
curling her red hair for work.

And his father laid down on the sofa
three months ago and died. So,

he sneaks his bowl
over to the sugar drawer.

THEODICY

JOE WILKINS

Stars like you've never seen stars.

I mean it.

We were some miles out on the far prairie—
a track of gravel we called a road,
little tufts of bunch grass, pear cactus,
sage blue-silver and burled,

a dry creek sweeping down from the hills,
the cutbank we leaned up against.

And that burn of stars—

I'm telling you they were the seraphim's choir of true light.
Bright, I'm telling you. Light like God's good
word, his native tongue,

his one fiery, sanctified song in the dark.

We split between the four of us—
we were eleven then, or maybe Vinny was just ten—
that backpack full of warm beers we'd filched
from Cotton Pinkerton's old man,

who we knew would wake tomorrow afternoon
hungover and shit-dumb as ever,
chasing snakes, sure he'd drunk it himself.

Anyway, we did what we were supposed to do—

we chugged suds, we laughed, we spoke words not fit
to be words. Laughed some more. Bill and I clambered
up the cutbank and stood at the dirt lip of it,
our little peckers in our hands.

There, we pissed perfect, crystalline arcs
out into that enkindled night—

and down over Vinny and Cotton,
both pawing by starlight the glossy tits of some centerfold.
Do you see what I'm saying?

Strike us down. You might as well. A few years later
Bill quit school and dedicated himself to methamphetamine.
Cotton ended up in Iraq. He is still in Iraq.
He fucking loves it there.

And Vinny—
who if I get right down to it was probably just ten,
who beneath his right eye had this sloppy
jackknife scar that slid down his cheek
and went red and loud near his ear—
who knows about Vinny.

I know about the stars.
That night they made shadows of us,
made us bigger, wilder than we were—

blue-silver as the sage,
edged as the creek's steep cutbank,
more alive, more holy, closer by far to God
than any-goddamn-thing-else out there—

grass, pear cactus, rot-wood tumble of a homesteader's shack,
the far-off, sorry, star-strangled lights of the crossroads town
we called home—

they loved us, those stars.

They must have, anyway, for they did
what no one did, what even we
could not:

they saw us
and spared us.

Joe Wilkins is the author of a memoir-in-fragments, *The Mountain and the Fathers* (Counterpoint 2012) and a collection of poems, *Killing the Murnion Dogs* (Black Lawrence Press 2011). His poems, essays, and stories have appeared in the *Georgia Review*, the *Southern Review*, *Harvard Review*, the *Sun*, *Orion*, and *Slate*, among other magazines and literary journals. He lives with his wife, son, and daughter on the north Iowa prairie, where he teaches writing at Waldorf College.

LITERARY SHORT STORY: A MAD LIB

MATTHEW BURNSIDE & KAT LEWIN

_____
ONE WORD TITLE

The evening was _____ and the _____ resembled a
WEATHER INDICATIVE OF THE PROTAG'S INTERNAL STATE   MOON

chipped saucer poised to_____
FORESHADOWING OF INCEST, ABORTION, RAGING LATENT HOMOSEXUALITY, THE DEATH OF

_____ over the city. _____
A PET AND/OR ALL OF THE ABOVE   PROTAG: HE OR SHE. ANTECEDENTS ARE FOR GENRE FIC.

absently stroked the _____ as he/she thought about
SELF-CONSCIOUSLY QUIRKY OBJECT SYMBOLIC OF HAPPIER TIMES

_____. He/she couldn't keep his/her eyes off the _____ sunset. It was like a
SOME STUFF IN SUMMARY   SEPIA

_____.
METAPHOR THAT DOESN'T QUITE FIT

Seven long years. The old neighborhood wasn't the same anymore. Things were _____ now,
ADJECTIVE

_____. *Seven years is seven years too long*, he/she_____
SYNONYM   'THOUGHT' IS TOO EASY. HOW ABOUT 'RUMINATED'?

"_____," Ron grumbled as he/she walked in through the door.
WITTY DIALOGUE, PREFERABLY IN A SOUTHERN ACCENT

His _____ shirt was streaked with chewing tobacco. He returned to his _____
    SEPIA   SOCIO-ECONOMIC STATUS INDICATOR

in the living room, where he proceeded to pack a mouthful of Skoal into his cheeks.

"_____," _____ reparted.
  CLEVER REPARTEE   PROTAG

"_____," Ron stormed _____.
  SEEMINGLY INNOCUOUS PHRASE   ADVERBIALLY

His _____ eyes _____
  SEPIA   FIXATION ON EYES

_____
           ...THEY SAY EYES ARE THE WINDOWS TO THE SOUL, YOU KNOW...

_____. He/she watched the _____ glint off of Ron's eyes, and as a sheen of tears
  ...HOLD TIGHT. ALMOST DONE.   MOON

covered the _____ orbs of Ron's _____, he/she saw his/her own
       POETIC ADJECTIVE   HEART/SOUL/OCULAR CAVITIES

reflection in them. When did his/her _____ get so _____?
                        ONCE ATTRACTIVE FEATURE   SAGGY/WRINKLED/STICKY

Just then, he/she realized _how distorted we all are in another's eyes._
                OH SNAP, YOU SEE WHAT I DID THERE? WORDSMITH!

The _____. Suddenly, Ron chortled. "Also,
          SHIT, TIME TO WRAP THINGS UP. MAYBE SOMETHING SHOULD HAPPEN.

I sold the house today. Got a good deal on 'er. Surprise! We're moving to Florida." Ever since Ron was young, he

had dreamed of moving to Florida. *Ah, Florida. The* _____ *State.* As he watched the _____ day wind
                                        SEPIA   WEATHERY

down through the blinds, he quickened the pace of his chewing from a lazy, cud-like roll to a masticating frenzy.

He knew in his heart that _____
                              FUCK. THIS ISN'T RON'S STORY. WHAT HAPPENED TO THE PROTAGONIST? OF COURSE I KNOW

_____.
  WHAT PSYCHIC DISTANCE IS.

"I'm glad we won the lottery, Ron, but I'm not going with you. I've been meaning to tell you. I'm

_____."
  PREGNANT/GAY/DEAD/SEPIA

Outside, a wolf crossed the road. Inside, on the kitchen table, _____ wobbled
                              SENTIMENTAL OBJECT FROM FIRST PAGE

on the edge of the table as though it were _____. "Well hell, I knew that. I think
                              SOMETHING POINTLESSLY AMBIGUOUS

the whole _____ neighborhood did," Ron said, choking on his tobacco. "_____
          EDGY EXPLETIVE   FOR A GUY CHOKING ON

_____."
  TOBACCO, HE SURE CAN SPEAK INTELLIGIBLY

Suddenly, they both heard something in the kitchen, like _____. They pushed open
                              REMEMBER THAT FORESHADOWING?

the door. A wolf stood gazing at them, a bloody heart in his mouth. For a long time he stood devouring the

_____ heart, gazing as though he knew _____.
   SEPIA   EVERYTHING I NEED YOU TO KNOW BUT MY CHARACTERS CANNOT SAY

Then, he left.

"Forget Florida," Ron said, "As long as I have _____
                                            A DEFT REVELATION WHICH COULD ONLY BE TRIGGERED BY A

_____ who needs Florida?"
    MOTHERFUCKING WOLF CHOMPING DOWN ON A MOTHERFUCKINGHEART

"_____," _____ said _____.
    REPETITION OF PREV. SEEMINGLY INNOCUOUS PHRASE   PROTAG   OPPOSITE-OF-PREVIOUS-ADVERB-IALLY

"_____," he/she repeated.
    REPETITION OF THE REPETITION

They stared out the window for a long time at the _____ _____. It was almost morning. <u>Money</u>
                                                  SEPIA   MOON

<u>couldn't buy you happiness.</u>
    OR VARIANT MORAL

Matthew Burnside has written words, letters, numbers, and symbols.

Kat Lewin is in the late experimental phases of trying to mate her Roomba with a typewriter. For science, mostly. Her fiction has been published in *Per Contra*, *Smash Cake*, and *decomP magazinE*. She is an MFA candidate at UC Irvine.

ROSES OF THE ORGANIC

SHIRA DENTZ

Stories told with beginnings, middles, and ends, and characters who want things.

PARIS

—   Backstage   Christian Dior's   designer   said   John Galliano, Dior's
designer, came out in a story about touch as well as sight — the models' bulb-shaped-like   iridescent   shine   to   be manipulated colors were a hothouse explosion of women   as   flowers.   Petals   lapped   in   cyberspace — gliding in front of a hand-painted pansy the parade did turn the show Monday into the breathing, heaving into the classic static audience.

here of night it is this loveliness

lemon in the side. surrounded by tree arms waving fat well that's a fact not a feeling somewhere to the side. surrounded by tree arms waving fat well that's a fact not a feeling some other like a bandage creeps up. telling me awake trees mountains and yes

sun. honey leaves. idea that someone put trees down separately, but white alpines root together underground. trees are like families, some planted in native soil, some in unison others not connected though part of a large   then there's wind blowing seeds like pines

lemon   in   the seltzer   keeping me   awake   tree arms waving fluctuating   fluxing the   shade   curdling   somewhere to the side. surrounded by trees mountains   and sky   here   sky   a drink   of   cool water
as usual am paranoid   in   regard   to some   people, jealous   in   regard to   others,   feelingfat   well   that's   a fact not a feeling and   yes   my mother   like   a bandage   creeps up.   telling   me she's   concerned about my weight there's   enough   to bombard   me when   i   think about   it/her   to make   my   mind shut   off.   but   i want   to   turn   it on.

THE SUN A NIPPLE OF LIGHT

SHIRA DENTZ

there's a price to pay for resisting, later, my mind somehow effected for having
pushed it over and beyond where it wanted to go. still windy out there clouds
thick and indistinguishable from snow on the mountains. when to use the article.
about now is when i'd check FB or email about now is when something from
pop culture would be inserted about now i say i don't like this coffee and about now i look
at the tree branches shaking in the wind. and say that i wish i had brought
my gym stuff because my stomach feels awful and fat. though who cares what it
feels like because no one's looking. possibly this is a catch-22 way of thinking. then
i think of s and my hurt feelings that she's ignoring my book. then i think of how
untruthful or unforward i've become now and how i used to hate that. i don't
out and out lie but am more circumspect. well again i want to check FB. it's like
an addiction? all these things are like drugs distractions to give me a hit of what? buzz?
sunlight for a second? on my table. will probably get dark again. again, FB. i
wonder if writers who are former cigarette smokers get more addicted to FB when
they write. so what if this has no value? why can't i just feel that it doesn't and stay
with it? most things aren't of value though they have some purpose. this seems
to have no purpose. except to me? now i think of emailing a who i haven't heard
from in a long time, by whom i also feel hurt. being ignored. this is the theme. is it
because i have to deal with my aloneness if i don't check my email etc.? now i think
of books that i want to read, like moby dick. yes, it would be luxurious to read right
now although i'm sure i'd get anxious about the time slipping by. now i want to
look at my gym's schedule?
is it the wind or an air vent? shadows and sun originating so far away affecting me
all the way down here. again, i want to check FB, my email. connection. writing is
solitaire. it's true this coffee is awful, i threw it out. i was thinking of writing this
about the coffee before i threw it out, so i dutifully recorded this thought even
though i was past it. i now have a can of ice cold diet coke nearby. i don't feel like
recording every movement. but now there's no sun either. i left the room with sun
and returned without. once again the pull to connect, a compulsion since there's
no real urgency. now i think of my friend l who i haven't talked to in months, it's
been at least two. you know what's coming. i felt that i needed to distance myself
from her manic depression. both sides seem to be pretty extreme. and now, again,
the pull. is it to feel reassured? blue band of sky. is everyone always tired? can i give

in to my pull now? yes, it's to feel less alone. i can check the weather. I can imagine the white globe light ahead as a skull. My mother, the flesh and blood person. My mother, the clouds covering the skies. J as a letter as a shape. I can't say we're made out of the same cloth, although I often feel that my body is hers, and sometimes something in my personality and I feel kind of dead, numb, implacable, when I feel this. Do I have an identity that's separate or is it a mix? another very successful poet wrote a book about being a mother. can i still write about my mother without being a mother myself? A beam of light in the jock jaw lock. rooting down in some mushrooms. is this about language or? sun again on a diagonal, warm on an arm. an avocado slice pulses in out bigger and the exhale of some mechanical pipes and the wind outside. all of this so boring.

i don't know how long it's been since i saw my father--the last time was when his mother died, and i don't know what year. my brother was still talking to me then so he was more like a line, a straight-edge. it's very painful to recount an example of what i mean and don't know if you'll find this interesting or something you'd rather skip over. a cousin of ours and his wife had a third baby who died, and my brother who's a psychiatrist and medical internist said he didn't understand what their fuss was about since they had had two other healthy kids. adding to this was the fact that in our own family a child had died, my brother---his brother, too, though he was a baby when my/our brother died. my brother and i did a birth dance when my second brother was born. it's this second brother who no longer talks to me. he's cleared the slate, i suppose. is he a line, still? i wonder what shape i am in his mind. i don't remember my sister at our grandmother's funeral, though I'm sure she was there. i remember my father telling me he was concerned about my teeth when he saw me, and that he'd be willing to pay for braces. I remember my brother being upset or angry or incredulous or a mix of these and telling me how my father had told him not to talk to him while he was praying, when my brother went to say bye. It seemed to my brother that after not having seen or talked to him for many years, that my brother was more important than my father praying and he should have stopped right then and listened to my brother. I can't say that I disagree. I suppose my father has had a few moments in which he could've said something that would have resulted in some kind of rapprochment, to use a psych word. But my father can't go that n-th degree. I understand how the older one gets it's harder and harder to even make a move like that--it's as though you're paralyzed, in a coma, and you can hear other people talking and would like to say something, but you can't. There's this split off people have even when they're not diagnosably in a coma; an inside and an outside, and loss of trust is as imparing as neural damage. Like a side of your jaw and lip are numb after dental work—you know it but can't make feeling happen.

i didn't inherit anything sentimental from any of my relatives. any sentiment is self generated, not any mythic lore supported by other family members; a community, if you will. i have a pillow that my grandmother's sister embroidered and she was murdered by nazis. murdered is different than killed. murder seems to accompany a premeditated plan. my grandmother left me a ring but i gave it to my sister—why did i do that? all these writing exercises suggest writing about relatives as though everyone has inherited sentimental objects and close family ties.

i even have to hide the sun in order to continue here. i drew the shade down but now a cloud's passed over the sun anyway. there's something about artificial heat that makes me sleepy. i am imagining piles of melting snow when i look out the window, white gleaming in the sunlight.

Shira Dentz is the author of a book of poems, *black seeds on a white dish* (Shearsman Books), a chapbook, *Leaf Weather* (Tilt Press), and a forthcoming collection, *door of thin skins* (CavanKerry Press). Her poems have appeared in *The American Poetry Review, The Iowa Review, jubilat*, and *New American Writing,* and have been featured at the *Academy of American Poets, NPR, Poetry Daily*, and *Verse Daily*. She holds a PhD. from the University of Utah and is currently book review editor at *Drunken Boat*.

[UNTITLED]

MAUREEN MCHUGH

Maybe your life needs an accident. Maybe bird-bone, the skin thin, the hair cut in the bathroom sink with a butcher's knife. Some say misery. Some say *quiet grace,* how the eldest sister loved the ocean *but never [thought] about it.* This life simple with water & dirt. This life saved & calm & secret. The feet washed in the sink, the curtains open, the sister saying *it's spelled exactly the way it sounds*

Maureen McHugh received her MFA from the University of Arizona where she held an 1885 Fellowship. She was the 2009 Prague Summer Program Fellowship winner, and has received a Pushcart Prize nomination. Other work can be found in *Third Coast*, *Conjunctions*, and *elimae*.

GETTING THE DRIFT

BRYAN ESTES

My father is kneeling right now in a memory, his arms elbow deep
in the chest cavity of a deer, his hands gripping heart and lungs,
telling me, *You have to squeeze and pull.* So easily

he navigated through the dense forest of masculinity,
a wet finger to the air, and a map of the stars
imprinted inside of his skull, his thick skin smelling of metal and oil.

A father, it seems, is any man who can build life
from a scrap heap, using only a pair of pliers and a plumb-bob,

whose mind is chambered and valved—his love carbureted
in proportion to fear, so that with his affection he creates a distance,
decades muffled in that part of the vehicle you never see.

At eight, I knew nothing of gravity's equations, but found loft
in a dead seagull's wings, and I knew the feeling
of calluses in my palm, and the sound a hammer doesn't make
when it finds a thumb.

With his hands, my father taught me
how to frame a discussion out of silence, and he showed me
the units of measurement, the tiniest fractions
between working and broken,
and how kind of right is equal to mostly wrong.

Soon enough I would whittle my way into the quiet center of a decade,
so I could measure the power of distance, and see for myself
how a continent drifts into the sea, to stand alone
on the shore, and bend my ear
to the many languages of departure.

Bryan Estes studies poetry among the corn and coal of the Middle West. He has read poems appearing in *Ploughshares*, *AGNI*, *Crazyhorse*, *The Kenyon Review*, and elsewhere.

IF I DIDN'T HAVE DOLLIES

ELIZABETH HARPER

If I didn't have
dollies
I would have to
bring people home
and kill them
and stuff them
so that I could
hold them
anytime
I wanted.
They would be mine
always.
And never
could they leave.
I would keep them
on the couch
and carry them
to bed
and touch them
anywhere
I wanted and
they would be
mine mine mine.

So the next time
you feel
like ridiculing
someone
for collecting
dolls,
or anything
for that matter,
just remember
the lives
that are saved
when things
are collected
rather than
human bodies.

Elizabeth Harper lives in Chicago where she writes poetry and reads it in bars, and sometimes cafes, art galleries, and churches. She has read at many venues around town including Weeds, Trace, Heartland Cafe, Cafe Ballou, and Black Rock. She has participated in the Chicago Calling Arts Festival and The Poetry Bomb several years running. Her two books of poetry are *Love Songs from Psychopaths* and *Fairy Tales Gone Awry*. She currently hosts a monthly open mic variety show at Phyllis' Musical Inn called "Elizabeth's Crazy Little Thing." She's tickled pink to have her poem included in *PANK*.

ANAGRAMS

DAIVA MARKELIS

Couples should never go to bed angry with each other.

There are times I'm so angry I lie in bed next to my husband, my body warped with rage, and think of clever, hurtful things to say. There are times he's so angry he pushes me away when I try to apologize. This makes me even angrier. I start throwing pillows or I turn the radio on full blast and start dancing on the mattress, novelty dances from the Sixties and Seventies—the Hitchhike, the Monkey, the YMCA.

"You're going to break the bed," he yells.

Sometimes he starts laughing and pulls me down by a leg and I know he's not angry anymore.

■

Couples should never threaten divorce in the heat of an emotional moment.

"I will divorce you," I tell my husband when he asks me to turn down the television because he's on the phone. He starts yelling. I tell him to use the cell. He swears. I run to the phone. "D-I-V-O-R-C-E," I spell into the receiver, especially when I know someone important is on the other line. To his credit, my husband never says he will divorce me, even when he finds crumbs on the bed or unwashed coffee cups lined up on a shelf behind a row of canned tomatoes like soldiers in some guerilla kitchen war.

■

A shared sense of humor is important to a happy marriage.

I love sophisticated British humor.

My husband prefers puns.

"A hole has been found in the nudist camp wall. The police are looking into it," he'll say. Or, "The best way to communicate with fish is to drop them a line."

I ignore his puns. I don't want to encourage him. This makes him angry. "I should at least get a groan. Or a courtesy laugh."

We argue about the concept of the courtesy laugh.

"You give your friends a courtesy laugh when they tell jokes that aren't funny," he claims.

"My friends don't tell jokes. They're naturally funny."

I feel bad when I say things like this. Luckily, I know what makes my husband happy. A game of Scrabble. My husband is a Scrabble genius; give him a seven letter word like PRESENT and he'll come up with its anagrams in seconds: PENSTER, SERPENT, REPENTS. He comes up with little stories to teach me the anagrams: "Think of the first chapter of the Bible. The snake, or the SERPENT, REPENTS because the Old Testament writer, the PENSTER, is there. He's PRESENT."

"Except in the Bible the serpent doesn't repent. In fact, he's responsible for the downfall of man."

"Well, maybe if there'd been a better penster present….."

When we play Scrabble, my husband usually wins. I try to distract him with small talk and, sometimes, puns: "How do you like my rack?" I say, pointing simultaneously to my breasts and my Scrabble tiles. This makes him angry, almost as angry as when I place one of the tiles on the board upside down "accidentally."

He lugs around a Scrabble board the way some men carry condoms. "You never know when you'll get lucky," he says.

■

Married couples respect each other's differences.

"You should read more high-quality literature," I tell my husband.

"I read the newspaper."

"Newspapers don't count."

"You're a snob," he says.

"Why won't you let yourself be moved by the power of the word?"

"I am moved by the power of the word," he says. "I play Scrabble. And I anagram."

"Some couples read aloud to each other before going to bed," I moped one time.

He came to bed that evening with a book from which he read in a slow, dramatic tone:

"With a long wood and playing with water to the right, most players will tend to keep the shot left. Subconsciously they'll turn on the shot to keep it from going into the water. You have to work against what your subconscious wants to do with the ball."

He paused, pleased with himself.

"My subconscious," I answered, "wants to take the ball and squeeze it really really hard."

■

Jealousy destroys relationships, signifying insecurity and lack of trust.

I sometimes dream that my husband is with another woman, someone younger and thinner and more athletic. Someone who appreciates his puns. I wake up angry and worried. I nudge my husband from his peaceful sleep.

"What is it?" he asks.

"I dreamt you were cheating on me," I say. Sometimes I smack him on the shoulder.

"I can't help what you dream," he says, annoyed.

I tell him my theory: one person's state of mind while sleeping—his thoughts and desires—can permeate another's dreams: "Like a bird flitting from a nest to a favorite tree."

"You're crazy," he says.

I describe the woman, some amalgam of who I think I should be, some nonexistent woman neither of us knows.

"You dream about Paul Konerko," my husband counters.

In my dreams, the White Sox first baseman tells me he desires as his life's companion not his young, slim, sane wife, but an overweight, angry, menopausal woman. The dreams always end with his wife busting in on us, shocked not so much that Pauly is in bed with another woman, but that the woman happens to be me.

■

Couples should not complain about each other's personal quirks.

"You're the only woman I know who gets a headache after sex," my husband says.
"It's a migraine."

"Are you a migraine imaginer?"

"What?"

"It's an anagram. Migraine. Imaginer. You know, like *penster present*."

"Do you anagram when we make love?"

He averts his eyes.

"Tell me," I say slowly, my voice rising. "Do. You. Anagram. When. We're. Making. Love."

He looks down at his feet.

"Almost never."

I called him an *overidle evildoer* and start throwing pillows and dancing on the mattress.

"You're going to break the bed," he yells.

He starts laughing and then I start laughing and very soon neither of us is angry anymore.

Daiva Markelis is professor of English at Eastern Illinois University, where she teaches creative writing, composition and rhetoric, and women's memoir. Her short stories have been published in *Cream City Review* and *Other Voices*. Her creative nonfiction has appeared in *The Chicago Tribune Sunday Magazine*, *The Chicago Reader*, *The American Literary Review*, *Crab Orchard Review*, *Writing on the Edge*, *Women and Language*, *Mattoid*, *Agora*, and *Fourth River*. Her memoir, *White Field, Black Sheep: A Lithuanian-American Life*, was published in 2010 by the University of Chicago Press.

SONG

DEREK HENDERSON

Water flows. And now we sing perhaps too warily, keeping track of water's overflow. Breakage lovely and scattered: coke bottles and chalk. Crazed cityscapes (the streets are flooded, water hard to be held; water flows below its film, off the surface all is nicked and photographed as a word) blossoms lift off a branch, the same as the waters. Word breaks first in water. Songs come stiff, strong drink, sung with warmth; each crowns the previous.

Water is a flame. It burns as much as song yearning at its surface, acute and watery. Its colors favor breakage: bubble and cease, bubble and cease. The city before it is brief (life in flame, traffic relatively useless) film its sea-green windows which raise the state of the film, seamless purity of sameness with the water. Water is breakage in a word, I sing more regularly now, life is severer now, nothing but air in the vents and the relentlessness of song.

All water is river. The tallest mountains equal a crack in God, they are so much superficial sucking at the river. The core is my favorite place of breakage: all the chattery flow that comes out is heat. The city escapes, briefly (the roads are rivers too, and traffic pulls me into its flux); picture this — green water flowing over nothing but film, to continue in the sheer sameness of its own wateriness. Water is the hum of broken words. As we take two or three steps from the stark shore, life has no more heat than a cancelled first breath.

The water in the river. As full of movement
as what two sets of eyes can see on the surface
of broken water. Colors perforate each breakage:
I can no longer call out in this heat. Brief cityscapes cross the surface (its streets like a river,
the traffic its flow); passage of liquid-blue-green:
in the same way we photograph nothing
in its completeness in order to sculpt our senses
in the sameness and continuity of water. Water
is a verb of breakage. What calls us to pair,
what calls us to three is rigid, severe: life is
heat and its richness can't be seen by one person.

Hot water still splits me open. So there's nothing else left like the water that falls too hot to clean me as hot as the water was. My favorite clarity is breakage: the house opens me up to chalk on the sidewalk. Cut out the cityscape (the street cuts me off from houses across the street; the wall is not good neighbor; the storm drifting in, though, that I can handle); water will grow between us, a film that will wrap us up every night that water falls, the sluice continues to say what it has to say and the water we've got will get so hot as to burn us. Hot water works through houses and brings on breakage. Lay this out twice or thrice, it is still a grinning sign, strong and level with warmth I've already told you about.

Water is violent. Here it thickens in the channel and I see fish surface twice, searching water's height. They prefer breakage over color: their mouths taste air and call for change. Their brief passage into the breath of the city (the river is a road that flows, traffic troubles its surface only); their watery breath of the film below is nothing but everything—a camera can't make certain that moment they end the sameness of water. Water is always a word of breakage. The fish get a second chance and at the third are caught, go rigid, dead, they follow a road of riches to get them back to their start.

Derek Henderson lives and writes in Salt Lake City, where the mountains still astound him after eight years. He is co-author, with Derek Pollard, of *Inconsequentia* (BlazeVox, 2010), and author of *Thus &*, an erasure of Ted Berrigan's *The Sonnets* (If P Then Q, 2011). He is also glad that William Carlos Williams says "I am that he / whose brains are scattered / aimlessly." You can find him online at www.twodereks.com.

THE SINS OF MY FATHER

ASHLEY C. FORD

I am obsessed with my father. I think of him multiple times a day each day. On a day when someone asks me about him, the rate of thought quadruples. I've written more about my father than any other topic. I gather facts about him the way some people gather useless trivia to spout on dates and in the middle of boring parties. I have learned he's funny. He went to prison when I was six months-old. He's written me letters most of my life. I have written him back four times. I do not think I am angry with him. Sometimes I think I miss him, and then I wonder if you can miss something you never had. And then I answer that question with experience. He is an artist and a Christian. For years, I've lied to people and told them I don't know why he is in prison. I do know. He is a convicted (and confessed) rapist. He also happens to be my muse.

How much can a father affect a child in 6 months? How much can his absence affect her in 23 ½ years? If you wrote my name on a chalkboard and had my family and friends list words they would use to describe me beneath it, I can guarantee "funny" would be a recurring adjective. Do I get that from him? My mother says that I'm a dreamer like him. She said he used to go to McDonalds, buy two cheeseburgers, eat them in the park and just daydream. He sketched my face before I was born. It doesn't look anything like me.

I'm not sure what all the daddy issues are but I don't think I suffer from them. The stereotype for a woman with daddy issues doesn't seem to match my thoughts or behaviors. I've not had a vast array of sexual partners, but I do have an abnormally high sex drive. Of this I am aware. I believe it's because I find comfort in sex along with pleasure. Yes, the physical act of copulation is outstanding, but it also feels good just to be that close to another human body. I derive more pleasure from a hand on my face than one on my ass. When you touch my face, it feels like you want all of me, especially the places other hands have overlooked. I don't sleep with men who haven't touched my face. My mother says my father was always taking me places, so excited to show me off, he'd forget to wash my face. Does that make this a daddy issue?

I've visited my father in prison once that I can remember. I was twelve. I know there were other visits before this, but I don't remember them. This one was the last. Before I knew what he'd done to end up prison. Right before Christmas, my birthday, the first real big snow of that winter, my Uncle Clarence picked me and my brother up from our home. My uncle recorded me singing "Silent Night". He told me my father would love my singing. I decided I had a terrible singing voice. We spent the night at his house in Elkhart, and went to the prison the next morning. My father didn't know we were coming.

The prison visitors were crowded into a cramped holding area. It was the space you stood and waited while the door behind you was locked, and then the door in front of you was opened to your loved ones/inmates. It was

prison purgatory. Staring through the glass, I found my father. He was already looking at me. He found my eyes and held onto them. He was surprised by our visit, but not by me. He knew me. When the doors opened I walked toward him wordlessly. He opened his arms, I laid my head on him and, in a room of convicted felons, found the only place I'd never be anxious to move on from. How can I explain how it felt? The best I can do is this:
Imagine I bake you a cake. Imagine this cake has many layers. Imagine each layer was a different time someone said I love you/I'm proud of you/You're amazing/You're the most important/You are my everything/I can't live without you/I made this for you/I miss you/You're beautiful/I will never leave you/ I will always, always always etc. Now, imagine I slice that cake. Imagine you eat it. Imagine its warm center. Imagine how it makes you full, but not too full, but so full you might never crave another piece of cake ever again. Imagine you never tasted cake like this before, but you heard of it. That others ate this cake so often, they would probably see nothing special about your consumption. Now rub your belly and smile. Think this cake is enough. That it will always be enough.
It was something like that.

I didn't find out my father was a rapist until I was 14 years-old. My grandmother blurted it out over orange chicken in a mall food court. My lo mein stopped moving past my tongue. I couldn't show too much emotion. In my family, showing too much emotion got you labeled. I was constantly fighting to have my "too sensitive" label stripped from my headboard and crying between bites of Asian food prepared by white teenagers wouldn't help my campaign. I rubbed my then fairly flat stomach. I told my grandmother I was full, that I couldn't eat another bite. I did not lie. For most of my life, up until the food court confession, I'd wondered what my father had done. I didn't worry much and rarely out loud to anyone other than my brother. I didn't know how bad it was or how much I really wanted to know. I just knew I didn't want it to be rape.

My body started to develop abnormally early. I started menstruating when I was eight and had breast by the time I was nine. Men noticed. Not boys. *Men.* My mother was extremely paranoid about molestation (with good reason, I suppose) and constantly drilled me with questions about who may or may not have been touching me. She also pointed out the clothes I wore (at nine) and how those clothes could entice the opposite sex. Let me say that I believe with all my heart that my mother intended to make me feel safe, to let me know she was looking out for me. Unfortunately, her interrogations made me feel as if should something happen to me, I had done something wrong. I should have seen it coming or I shouldn't have worn *that* dress. So, when something did happen to me, I didn't tell her. It also happened to be the one time she didn't ask.

My young adult life was riddled with instances of boys or men commenting on, touching, or ogling my body, and the people who should have stood up for me, shaming me intentionally or unintentionally. There was the time a boy put his hand down my shirt in the sixth grade. I told the principal, the boy was kicked out of school for 3 days, and for 3 days people came up to me and told me I'd made a big deal out of a harmless joke, that it meant nothing. Someone else's hands on my body meant nothing. When I was twelve and out of town with family, a man stopped me in a hotel elevator, asked me to come back to his room. I told him I was twelve. He asked me what my mama was feeding me to make me look so grown, repeated the offer to come back to his room. I rode the elevator back to our hotel room, changed into baggy jeans, refused to go back down to the lobby. At thirteen, I was chased home from the library by a car-full of teenage boys who attempted to pull me into the car and didn't stop until they were spooked by another car driving down the road we were on. The other car did not stop. Then there was the time a boy put his tongue in my mouth at the water fountain. I told family. They told me it would be an excuse for the school system to punish another little black boy. They told me to say nothing. These were adults. I was a child. I listened.

There is a very loud voice in this world that tells girls and women there is something about a man and sex that makes it impossible for him to control himself. When we are learning to be women the first thing we're told to do is cover up. Not for ourselves, our own modesty or comfort, but as not to draw the lingering eyes of men who would seek to hurt us. It is never about us learning about ourselves, only about us protecting ourselves. Protecting what we are raised to think is of the utmost importance; our sexual innocence.

Finding out my father was a rapist was like vomiting up the cake and realizing it was laced with shards of sea glass. All those blues, purples, oranges, and yellows sullied and staring up at me from the space between my fear of men and my love for my father, reflecting a truth I couldn't know before that moment. It all made sense. My father was a rapist and I was raped. I was familiar with the bible, had even signed one of those abstinence pledges at youth group. I knew about the sins of the father and what that meant for the child. I knew what my father did came back on me. He had hurt those women and I had been hurt. I convinced myself again, this wasn't the fault of the man who assaulted me. It was my own. My fault by the circumstances of my birth.

These are not things that I believe anymore. I know now that I can not blame myself for the crimes, not misunderstandings or harmless jokes, but **crimes,** committed against me. No man is without the agency to control his sexual urges, and if I do not give explicit consent for him to touch my body, he is violating my rights as human being by doing so. I know that my father is a rapist. I know that what he did changed the course of my life, but it did not give anyone permission to assault me. I know that he affected me. That I will always love hands on my face and always worry that I'll meet the women, or children of the women, he assaulted. I know that even though I love him, I can not release him from blame and take that onto myself. I can not have my cake. I've already eaten it.

I've been thinking about these things a lot because of a *New York Times* article about the rape of an 11-year old girl in Cleveland, Texas and the level of response to it. All I can think about is this child whose life will never be the same. I wonder how she'll deal with it. I wonder what I would have done if my tragedy had become such media fodder. I wonder how my family would have reacted had I given them the opportunity to react. I wonder how I address my victimization without living the "victim stereotype" because I don't have Lifetime Movie flashbacks and I'm not afraid of sex. I wonder if the person who harmed me is really "living with this for the rest of his life". I wonder if I'm really okay or if one day I will go batshit crazy and all those "daddy issues" and those "victim issues" and those "I've-gone-through-something-too-many-women-go-through issues" will come to the surface. I wonder what I'll do with them all.

I wonder what will protect me then.

Ashley Ford suffers from abibliophobia. She writes to soothe anxiety. She is a student at Ball State University and her work is featured in the spring 2011 edition of *The Broken Plate*. When she isn't volunteering, sewing, or stalking DIY design blogs, she contributes to VouchedBooks.com and TheChicklitz.com.

ELIZABETH BENNET WAKES IN A COLD SWEAT

ANDREA HENCHEY

Think quickly. No. Think thickly. Sickly. No.
Quick thinking. Thickets. Quickly through thickets.
Think: Cricket or croquet? Sashay? No, curtsy.
Curtsy cutely. Sweetly. Be pretty. Witty. Clever.
Quick. Charming. Charmed. Lucky. Lovely.

Faster! Think quickly! Sink quickly. No. Quicksand.
No. The more you…No. Sand. Think: Thick sand. So.
Quicksand. The dunes. I'm knee-deep, needy. Now
drowning. It's noon. And see how the vultures do circle.

Andrea Henchey holds an MFA in Creative Writing from Pacific Lutheran University; her work has appeared in *Absent* and *Ghoti* and is forthcoming in *H_NGM_N* and *A River & Sound Review*. Though her travels have brought her to more exotic locales such as Nepal, Kenya, and Chile, she currently lives in Connecticut where she coordinates "Inescapable Rhythms," a poetry reading series, trains for marathons with her mutt, Bodhisattva, and teaches full-time. Learn more at andreahenchey.com.

EL INFIERNO TAN TEMIDO

EDMUNDO PAZ SOLDÁN

a J. C. Onetti

Cuando le llegó la fotografía, en un sobre con un par de estampillas verdes y sellado en Bahía, cuando vio los cuerpos desnudos y los rostros sudorosos y obscenos, supo que era el comienzo, que habrían más fotografías de ella y de hombres extraños en el devenir de los días. Supo, también, que ella todavía lo amaba y que esa foto era la prueba más palpable de su amor; no podía estar equivocado: ella le había enseñado a leer a Onetti.

Ella lo había traicionado sin dejar de amarlo y se lo dijo. El no la perdonó y la apartó para siempre con un insulto desvaído, una sonrisa inteligente, un comentario que la mezclaba con todas las demás mujeres. Ella se fue de Cochabamba y dos meses después envió la primera fotografía. Las siguientes, cada vez más obscenas, fueron llegando desde Asunción, Buenos Aires y Santa María, a direcciones diferentes: a su pensión, a un compañero de trabajo, a la madre de su primera esposa. Después su única hija recibió una foto; pero él no haría como Risso, no se suicidaría: esperaba las fotos con alegría más que con temor, cada foto era la certificación de un rito, un elogio al complejo absurdo del amor creado por los hombres.

Sin embargo, las fotos dejaron de llegar. Y él esperó dos años y comprobó que era suficiente; sabía que la segunda desgracia, la venganza, era esencialmente menos grave que la primera, la traición, pero también mucho menos soportable; ahora había aprendido que la espera era mas intolerable que la venganza, que la traición, que cualquiera de las acciones humanas que poblaban el universo.

Era suficiente. Y se tragó todos los sellos de somníferos de todas las farmacias que conocía.

THE HELL MOST FEARED

TRANSLATION BY KIRK NESSET

When the photo appeared in the envelope affixed with green stamps, postmarked Bahía, when he saw the naked bodies and sweaty nasty faces, he knew the thing had begun—there'd be more pictures of her with strange men in the future. He also knew she still loved him, knew the picture was the most tangible test of his love. There could be no mistake: he'd given her Onetti to read.

She had betrayed him but continued to love him, and told him so. He hadn't forgiven her. With a vague insult and a knowing smile, he'd left her forever, tossing her into the pot with all other women. She had left Cochabamba. Two months later the first photograph came. The photos that followed, each more obscene than the last, were mailed from Asunción, Buenos Aires and Santa María, each to different addresses: one to his *pension,* one to a colleague at work, another to his first wife's mother. Later, his only daughter received a picture. Despite all, he wouldn't do what Risso, Onetti's character did—he would not commit suicide. He awaited the pictures with more pleasure than fear; each validated a ritual, a tribute to love, that absurd convention invented by man.

But the pictures stopped coming. He waited two years and realized that this would be all: realized that the second wound, vengeance, was finally less severe than the first, betrayal, and yet was less bearable, too. Expectation, he learned, was far worse than vengeance, or betrayal, or any other human action infusing the cosmos.

So enough was enough. He gathered all the sleeping pills he could find from every drugstore he knew and swallowed them all.

EL ENCARGO

EDMUNDO PAZ SOLDÁN

Solicitaron sus servicios para eliminar a una persona por quien sentía un aprecio particular. Enfundado en su vasto silencio y esbozando un leve gesto de duda, recibió el adelanto convenido. Como siempre, no preguntó los porqué, aunque esta vez le hubiéra gustado hacerlo.

Por la noche, fue a un sórdido bar a tres cuadras de su departamento. Allá se encontró con Carlos, un amigo lo suficientemente lejano como para desconocer su oficio. Bebió, conversó, cantó con él hasta rayar el alba; antes de despedirse brindó por la salud de su víctima, y luego, sin explicaciones para Carlos, lloró.

Despertó al mediodía en la penumbra de su habitación, sumergido en su camastro con las ropas aún puestas y el crepitar de un incendio en la cabeza. Una ducha con agua helada lo reanimó por completo. Se despidió de Mariel, su esposa, y fue a cumplir el encargo.

Trató de disipar los vestigios de escrúpulo que aún le sobrevivían; luego, los ojos entrecerrados por la angustia, disparó. Al ver el rostro desencajado de su víctima, las comisuras de sus labios se contrajeron en desgarrada mueca de impotencia: yacía frente al espejo del baño, exánime. Mariel se había convertido en una hermosa y joven viuda.

CONTRACT

TRANSLATION BY KIRK NESSET

They hire him to eliminate a person for whom he feels a particular fondness. Veiled in great silence, entertaining faint hints of doubt, he receives the advance they agree on. As usual, he doesn't ask questions, though this time he would like to.

That evening, he visits a less-than-nice bar three blocks from his house. There he runs into Carlos, a friend distant enough to not know his business. He drinks and talks and sings with the man until dawn. Before saying goodbye, he proposes a toast to his victim's health; later, with no explanation to Carlos, he weeps.

He awakens at noon in his shadowy bedroom, buried under the covers with his clothes on, his head on fire. A freezing shower revives him completely. He says goodbye to his wife, Mariel, and leaves to fulfill the contract.

He tries to release his remaining misgivings. Later, eyes half-shut in anguish, he fires. And then wincing—powerless, broken—sees the twisted grin of his victim, laying lifeless now before the bathroom mirror. Mariel has become a young, beautiful widow.

LA FAMILIA

EDMUNDO PAZ SOLDÁN

¡Soy inocente, yo no maté a mi padre! exclamó mi hermano, desesperado, apenas escuchó la sentencia. Me acerqué a él, intenté infundirle ánimo, le dije que yo le creía (y era verdad: tenía la certeza de que no mentía), pero mis palabras eran vanas: su nuevo destino estaba sellado. Apoyó su cabeza en mi pecho, lloró.

Fui a visitarlo todos los sábados por la tarde, durante véintisiete años, hasta que falleció. En el velorio, al mirar su precario ataúd desprovisto de coronas y recordatorios, sentí por primera vez el peso amargo del remordimiento.

Edmundo Paz Soldán is author of nine novels and three short story collections, including *La materia del deseo*, *Desencuentros*, *Los vivos y los muertos,* and *Norte*. He received Bolivia's National Book Award in 1992 and 2003, and is recipient of the Juan Rulfo Award; he was also a finalist for the prestigious Romulo Gallegos Award. He was raised in Cochabamba, Bolivia, and lives now in the US, serving as Professor of Hispanic Literature at Cornell University. One of the few McOndo writers residing here, he is frequently called upon as the movement's spokesperson by the American media. His work has been translated into seven languages.

FAMILY

TRANSLATION BY KIRK NESSET

I'm innocent! my desperate brother exclaimed when the sentence was read. I did not kill my father! I stood beside him, hoping to cheer him. I believed him, I said, which was true; I was sure he hadn't lied. But my words didn't help: his fate was spelled out. He dropped his head on my chest, sobbing.

I visited him every Saturday afternoon for twenty-seven years. Then he died. At the funeral, seeing his meager coffin devoid of mementos and wreaths, I felt at last the bitter weight of regret.

Kirk Nesset is author of two books of short stories, *Paradise Road* and *Mr. Agreeable*, as well as a book of translations, *Alphabet of the World*, and a nonfiction study, *The Stories of Raymond Carver*. His book of poems, *Saint X*, is forthcoming. He is recipient of the Drue Heinz Prize in Literature, a Pushcart Prize, and grants from the Pennsylvania Council on the Arts. His stories, poems, translations, and essays have appeared in *The Paris Review, Southern Review, Kenyon Review, Gettysburg Review, American Poetry Review, Iowa Review, Ploughshares, AGNI, Prairie Schooner,* and elsewhere. He teaches creative writing and literature at Allegheny College, and is writer in residence at Black Forest Writing Seminars (Freiburg, Germany).

WHEN THE GIRLS ARRIVED IN COPENHAGEN

KEITH TAYLOR

and left the station, near midnight,
snow fell in soft piles on their hats
and backpacks.

No cars or people passed
while they walked
down the hushed streets.

Through windows without blinds or curtains
they could see Danes bathed in blue
television light

or quietly reading in uncluttered rooms
small novels perhaps about two girls
long ago walking through snow.

AT THE FLOWER MERCHANT'S IN TOULOUSE

KEITH TAYLOR

Basques and Spaniards, French peasants
not a generation removed from dirt floors
and speaking the old language of the South

yell at each other in the warehouse
beside the railroad tracks
where the flower wholesaler won't give me work

among all the red and yellow blossoms
brought north through the night
that must get cut

then wrapped before they wilt
and where scents rise in a mix strong enough
to turn the whole place quiet.

A RETURN

KEITH TAYLOR

When she bent over the twins
who were sleeping on the floor,
I thought that the sadness
and wisdom of her trip
still clung to her and hoped
for the time that would arrive
soon enough when she could be silly
again, loveably ordinary,
and I could look at her unafraid.

Keith Taylor published two books in 2011—*Ghost Writers*, an anthology of Michigan ghost stories co-edited with Laura Kasischke, and *Marginalia for a Natural History*, a chapbook of eight-line poems.

FROM "JESSE JAMES"

KEVIN WEIDNER

I know what it means to sheave to stand
as a shock of grain the land so much a part
it pains to leave & how many names I've had
& states I've been but only one I've held
inside my chest if I could only say how
this place got lodged inside my body
how it hangs heavy hollow or not the dirt
that bore me the river that feeds & where
I want to die is not here on his deathbed
he said this damned Nebraska land
just take me home when I unfold
a map my eyes settle into that place
& I don't know whether to say the name or lie
in the quiet to keep it always inside and here
I lie this body's weight and boot heel
still ground hard into my chest

FROM "JESSE JAMES"

KEVIN WEIDNER

I keep no record of where I've been
save the postmarks on letters I send & still
nobody has any idea where I'm headed
like tracking a wounded buck that crosses
these mountains in one great bound
I imagine the governor with his nose
to the ground & the bounty hunters
fingering their charms & the traitors' pockets
of stolen rounds but remember dear
I've been downed before I can breathe
with one leaking lung & there's an eagle
in the sky today with a wingspan to snuff
out the sun so I lie on my back counting
how many times he goes around & around

Kevin Weidner hails from Missouri and currently lives in Tuscaloosa, pursuing an MFA at the University of Alabama. He edits the online journal *751 Magazine*.

THERE IS NO PARKING FROM HERE TO CORNER

ALEXIS POPE

That stop sign nailed to the tree out front. He decided that meant go. Her feathered features weakened under his thumbs. Her chirps weren't heard as much as eaten. What he thought was a light snack was actually dinner. Her consumption so thorough and raw, as if the grill was never lit and he slopped it onto the paper plate. No grease to soak into. No heat to guard his tongue from. The nails in the tree watched as the feathers flew and no real songs were sung. It's not romance if it's modern, meaning if he didn't read it in a book somewhere by someone who wasn't dead. Afterward she considered burying the fallen feathers in the yard. The one behind the house that wasn't theirs. She already knew the paint colors she would coat the walls with, even though they were both unemployed. It's only rape if you don't want it. Although she thought this is what rape would feel like. So empty. Almost like dying without the death. But the sun was high at noon and there wasn't even a shadow. Only the loss of feathers, the flattening of grass, the metallic scent left behind. It was then she knew what their love was: a house with no owner.

AFTER WE FLATTENED THAT LAST PENNY

ALEXIS POPE

The railroad tracks that echo your forgotten whine. It's like the smell of rosemary never got washed off your fingerprints. There, that little pucker of skin tucked under your bra strap. The slight itch of a mosquito in the act. The pirouette of the leaf onto the puddle. It's all there in the backyard, right before the train tracks. The sound that woke you up at night. The pillow landing like a cinderblock on the shag rug. I felt like there was always a hole in the floor right here. It landed right here. I can still feel the dent of feathers, the heat of your night breath, the sugar of sleep crystallized on your left breast. There was that spot in the back yard, before the train tracks, before the dog shit, before the thunderstorm, before the pillow. The moss has buttoned up its over coat and the spot, well, I can barely find it. You must know this: that train still comes. It still screams out to your memory, still cries for your absent body. It still remembers you lived upstairs: past the backyard and after the tracks.

Alexis Pope isn't sure what to say about herself. She isn't normally this shy. She's said some stuff in >kill author, Red Lightbulbs, Midwestern Gothic, Requited, and elsewhere. Her favorite color is grass stain.

A LOVE POEM

RUSS WOODS

There are two men in an Aspen grove in Colorado and they are touching their foreheads together. Their foreheads are sweaty and their sweat mingles and drips down into the dirt and makes sweat-mud, which is saltier than regular mud. The men's foreheads and the men are in the grove and the grove is shaped like a forehead. The grove is next to a freshwater lake which is also shaped like a forehead and there is a town on the lakeshore which is inhabited by forehead-people. There is a mountain there called mount forehead and deer and bears and raccoons live on it. Somewhere there is a small country whose national bird is the forehead and the men, right now, are only speaking the native language of this country, and they are doing the national dance of this country, though they don't know it. I am watching these men from a forehead-shaped hot air balloon hovering over the aspen grove and you are with me and I want to kiss you on your you-know-what.

Russ Woods lives in Chicago where he co-edits the online literary magazine *Red Lightbulbs* with his wife Meghan Lamb. If he could be any plant, he wouldn't be a plant, he'd be a mushroom. He makes music in the band Pretty Swans.

TO WHOM THIS MAY CONCERN

CAMONGHNE FELIX

This morning I took a bath under an open roof. Check it: me, dressed in an immature pond, looking up at the earth—but school taught me to look down on it, so now I know to ask permission. Earth? Sky? Why you be so glass hungry? Why you be so ready to big up everything? Some things don't deserve cultivation—lets keep our garden private, just you and me? I live next to a safe-house for the deaf. Last night the thunder came without the big light, I was scared for them—how they know when the rain is coming? I know. I always know. My body holds ninety-two percent of its own water. I stand in the middle of the street—I buoy. I make my mouth a trademark, I lighthouse, I scream "land", I know bones all vibrate with me. You? You elite. You make me jealous. I don't get jealous. I wear all the nice things and hide.

VOWS

CAMONGHNE FELIX

You were the loudest man I had ever met;
A
crowded room,
a command,
a call for reception.

I watched you,
and nothing else
could have a language -
it was yours,
you were its proposal.

When watching a deaf
man learn to love a privilege
he cannot benefit from,
tell him he is the driver.
Tell him love is a taxi.
When it dies in his mouth,
he'll never know.

Before we taught our first
born to sign,
we taught her to
walk on her hands.
A calloused palm
is a hand bankrupted into
survival. You wanted to know
that she could barrel through
anything too silent. I told you
not to

Our baby's first word
was "winter".
In a span of an hour,
she slung it at
every wall
like her own song,
and you kept missing it.
What vehicle is
discourse if it faints before
its own obstruction?

When you left,
I taught her to sign
"Overwhelmed",
so that if you ever
came back,
I could say "See? We learned for you."

Camonghne Felix is a NYC grown cupcake enthusiast and college sophomore with neurotic tendencies. She writes about the small things that happen when we stop looking.

WILLOW

LAUREN BECKER

Willow is skinny. Willow is hungry. Willow is Wendy. Wendy wants Wendy's or Burger King or Olive Garden all you can eat pasta and bread sticks. Willow wants a tall non-fat latte and half of a pear.

Willow has stick-straight bangs and interesting jewelry. Her cheekbones hollow, collarbones warn. They could draw blood. She wears halter tops. They are sexy.

Willow does not like sex. She does it because it burns approximately 210 calories if she participates with that purpose.

The scale tells Willow which one she is. Bad Willow calls in sick, washes a laxative down with hot water with lemon and watches cooking shows. Good Willow goes to work in her favorite silk halter top under a tiny fitted jacket and the skinniest of jeans. She brings donuts for the break room. The kind with raspberry jelly or coconut. Willow doesn't like those kinds.

Willow eats lunch with girls who eat lunch. She wants a sandwich and chips. She eats her salad, each bite dipped in non-fat ranch dressing. She walks six city blocks in the rest of the hour, burning approximately 95 calories.

On her birthday, she eats a bacon cheeseburger and fries, with a chocolate cupcake for dessert. It hurts. She eats until it's all gone.

This is her routine. When she follows it, she is calm. She is calmer. Willow is never calm. Her body needs things.

Her body wants to like sex again. Her body wants to be warm. She doesn't want her body. Her body wants the other half of the pear.

ANNABEL

LAUREN BECKER

Annabel was cracked where no one could see. Hairline, but beneath. She waited for one of them to feel it. To say something. They never said.

She looked whole, which satisfied. Annabel wore cardigans with jeans, black or white tanks beneath. Slight hints of things. The unbuttoning of the sweater sacred. For them.

Her purse was brown. A name stitched on it. Not hers. Her name unusual enough that they had not met another. Most could spell it. In e-mails and texts where they said the things they couldn't. Mouths too greedy to spell the things she needed. They did not need those things. She stopped asking.

The crack came in seventh grade, when the math teacher she worshipped, worshipped back. He offered her time alone, something she did not get. Working parents. Brother with Down's Syndrome. They cared for him and sleepwalked the remainder of their awake hours. They gave her the name and soon had nothing left. She missed them like a distant season.

Annabel, he breathed, as he gave her more work, more instruction. He stood over her and gave her his attention. She took it. She gave back. She could not tell.

She told her secrets on paper and hid them. Nobody looked. Her retarded brother went through her things, looking for candy, not knowing how to enter and leave without fingerprints. She left chocolate bars and candy necklaces under her pillow. He left his imprint and wrappers on her bedspread. She slept curled in his rounded outline.

"Peter," she whispered, in his ear, while he watched cartoons. "Can you see it? The crack?" He smacked at her with his limp hand and demanded a bowl of cereal. Annabel brought him cereal, rich in sugar and vitamins, and watched him eat. She had mostly stopped, four years before, when she stopped doing math.

The teacher left her messages, still. He sent her letters. Annabel. Please. She recognized his attention now as a lure for theft. She ignored him and met men at gas stations and coffee shops. They thought she was in college. She was older than her history. They admired her name. They felt her hipbones beneath them and called it. She stopped waiting.

She traded the name for Ann. She began to do math again.

Ann started college, leaving behind relieved parents and candy, hidden with simple maps for her brother. She took the paper, weighty, along with towels and books and cardigan sweaters. She left the crack and made herself whole. It addressed itself in a letter she opened. She accepted it, familiar in the unknown place. Addressed to Annabel, she named herself familiar, too.

Lauren Becker lives in Oakland, California. She is editor of *Corium Magazine* and curator of the Bay Area reading series, East Bay on the Brain. Her work has appeared in the *Los Angeles Review, Pedestal Magazine, Wigleaf, Juked, Hobart,* and elsewhere. Her collection Things About Me and You is included in *Shut Up/Look Pretty* (Tiny Hardcore Press, 2012).

10 01

AWESOME WORDS CONTEST

JUDGE: MICHAEL MARTONE

WINNERS
1ST: TYLER GOBBLE
2ND: ERIN FITZGERALD
3RD: NAOMI DAY

TO TOSS IS TO LIFE

TYLER GOBBLE

Every third Tuesday, Karl and I carry his garbage to the corner. The bottom of a bag blows out. Karl looks for witnesses and the whole neighborhood stares at its feet. The corner is a sad place to be an object. No one's banana peels, old papers, broken desk lamps. My best thoughts come balancing pizza boxes with Karl. Karl likes that new kind of garbage truck with the forks longer than a human arm. I laugh as he mimics one, ripping open a trash bag with a rusty pipe.

Karl stomps like he owns this bridge. We walk in the middle. No cars on the midnight road. Karl tries to get every step right. Me, I'm inching my way along hoping to spot a pocketknife in the ditch. Karl picks out a large mouth gliding out of the water. Neither of us sees it land back in the water. Some things just seem to drift off, I start to say, but Karl has wandered ahead, out of earshot.

A family in a window is passing bread. I'm on tiptoes. Karl atop an old tire. There's an itch where you need to see others living happily. This block twinkles like in the photos, the oil slick puddles, the moon inching its way between the homes, some animal under a bush with hungry eyes. Karl says the edge of town is the best place to discover new life. When my calves grow tired, Karl squeezes my shoulder and says, let's go. I get what he's saying.

A can wallops my chest. Karl believes *catch* is an instinct, not a word. I never met Karl's mother and mine live in Oklahoma. He asks if they have soda in Oklahoma. Coca-Cola is my parents' favorite brand, their entire kitchen dedicated to soda. Karl asks if I'm gonna throw the can back or act like I never played Little League. I toss it back. Karl doesn't catch it, but disappears into a cornfield.

Backside of the cornfield, Karl sits in a blue car. Karl says, you drive. Somehow Karl works downtown. The struts he takes in his tie and slacks, make the walk look a block long. I want to ask him whose car this is, but he's in the passenger seat. Those little stickers—things in mirror are closer than they appear—shout warnings that don't even seem true anymore. Karl checks his face and gets out.

Karl's head like a skipping stone. The cornfield behind his house, a shadow mimicking life more than ever imagined. Pyramids of rocks dug up and piled, the work of Karl's hands. Reduced to a single one. Cars hear the ping, assume backfire, cowbell on the radio. They go off down the highway. To exist in a cornfield with a stone is fate. No more cars except one, like the top of the sun, hit by my first throw, the last rock. Sirens switch on, flickering stripes, the cornstalks shined into black. Mine, the body flat in the mud.

A cat I don't know brings me a dead rat. I wave my hand like dusting off an old book. The cat swallows the head. In their own way, they feed us, Karl says. The animals I knew were always hungry, treading paths in the yard. As a child, I was obsessed with the cats, how if you squeezed real tight, they hardly existed. Truth is pets seem destined to either do us in, or make our arms so warm from cuddling that we can't even stand it. That's why we're always tossing them away. Always, they know how to crawl back, Karl says.

Let out your cast and see where it flies, Karl says. Maybe stuck in a tree, but most things come back to where they came, surely, I hope. Two guys and two poles. To cast is to set life on a course of action. The fishing poles lean against a tree. Boredom wafts from the water. Karl clutches a pocketknife and a spear.

I met Karl's sister once. She didn't talk much, not because she was shy, Karl said, but because she was sad. She wore a polka-dotted dress. The beige carpet of his room is littered with small things. Mail that might contain a bill or maybe a check. Some remotes to TVs he doesn't own anymore. His wallet with more money and family photos than he'd admit. Karl says, remember that fish? I know where it went. I nod and put down the fingernail clippers, their shape indented in my palm. It got its neck caught in a piece of plastic in the river and died, Karl says.

The rain owns the bridge now. We're huddled under one umbrella, one streetlight. A car tosses a can into the river. We race to the edge to watch it sink. Karl says, I think I see a person down in the water. When the weather is nice, I always believe Karl. I wonder if the can was Coca-Cola. Karl heads off with the umbrella, tightrope-walking the centerline. I look into the river. I can't find the can.

Tyler Gobble is lead editor of Stoked Press and a contributor with Vouched Books. Find recent publications and other (maybe) neat things at www.tylergobble.com.

NO ONE CARES ABOUT YOUR PROBLEMS

ERIN FITZGERALD

Dover Plains

I've cashed two paychecks since the last time I saw you in person. You'd done your best, but you were always cut out of felt with left-handed school scissors. Your nubbly skirt hem and the grey of your carefully planned hairline were so far away from your natural part. But all of you was on the carpet, waiting for the limo to arrive.

I slipped past you so that I could go to the ladies' room and pray. I still don't know if you saw me.

Grove Street

This morning, the man in the blue Honda was wearing a blue chambray shirt and khaki pants. He had a styrofoam coffee cup in his left hand and his cellphone in his right hand. While he talked on his phone, his coffee fingers brushed against the steering wheel. While he sipped his coffee, his cellphone fingers brushed against the steering wheel. That work was never going to do itself.

Butter Brook

Three days in a row, at exactly 10:07am, I have received a call. The voice inside is polished to a dull shine. It springs locks and decodes messages thousands of miles away from where I stand, handset at my ear.

This is. A reminder. That your prescription is, ready! For pickup.

I always hang up before I'm told where the nearest pharmacy is. I'm afraid of what would happen if I didn't.

Mountain Rise

Four Christmases ago, I reached into my stocking and found a white box with a harmonica inside.

"What's this?" I asked my mom.

"You told me you wanted a harmonica."

"I don't think so."

"Well, now you have one."

I should have asked my sister if she'd asked for a harmonica. Instead, I took it home. It's on my bookshelf. When I breathe through it, everything is dark chocolate sauce on two dollar vanilla ice cream.

Erin Fitzgerald's stories have appeared in *Hobart, wigleaf, Monkeybicycle, Necessary Fiction, elimae, Word Riot, Corium*, and many other fine online literary publications. Her chapbook, *This Morning Will Be Different*, appears in the anthology *Shut Up/Look Pretty* (Tiny Hardcore Press). She is the lead editor of *The Northville Review*. Erin lives in western Connecticut, and online at rarelylikable.com.

A LIST OF MY SHORTCOMINGS

NAOMI DAY

1. Avocados: mushy, the rainbow's spectrum of green. Availing myself of the grocery store's stock, I come home and consume. After, I feel sick. At the doctor's, I'm told *no, not food poisoning.* Asking, *well, what the hell is it then?* Aversion like bittersweet milkweed I can taste through those arctic blue eyes.

2. Because of the miscarriage, we split. Before the miscarriage, we had buried troubles beneath black ice so thick we couldn't break through. Beyond the ice, there was only more darkness farther than Zach could possibly reach to save me. But after that? Because of the miscarriage, my heart sank in the ice.

3. Can't do it, I was told. Can't continue here. Can't do it! Can't keep on keeping on. Can't fucking breathe, it scares me. Can't someone help me?

4. Dreams are fires built of my imagination, lit with the matches of my subconscious. Does he love? Does he fear? Damn it, I do.

5. Empty four-way stops: wide, badly lit intersections. Envision all those mistakes I made. Ecstasy only lasted so long: now I'm stuck floating in blackness, a streetlamp on every one of the four corners. Each one flickers and burns out. Envy the younger self.

6. Finally I wanted to give up and let it go. Fantasies had taken me only so far, and I had a whole other journey to complete. Forget about it, okay?

7. Go, go, go away, go away baby. Granted, I didn't actually mean it: Yulia should have understood my secret desires. Gratification is something I am no longer permitted to have.

8. Hell must be cold and wet. Heaven must be warm and dry. Hell must be beneath the earth. Heaven must be above the earth. Hell must be ruled over by Heaven's evil brother. Heaven must be the ultimate destination. However, what if: Hell is warm and dry? Heaven is cold and wet? Hell is above the earth? Heaven is beneath the earth? Hell is the ultimate destination? Heaven is ruled over by Hell's evil brother? However, what if my whole life is a lie?

9. Imagination: life is your creation.

10. Jesus must be a lie: who'd let a baby die?

11. Kansas is one huge wasteland of depression. Kansas is where the broken dreams go to die. Kansas casts a shadow bigger than the entire world. Kansas has set its glittering sights on me and is calling me home.

12. Lithium: they were on it. Liam tried to convince me. Liam was a shooting star. Liam burned out before his time.

13. Maybe later I'll understand. Mighty and powerful isn't me: won't ever be me. My mind wants to blow me up.

14. Never let go: the tighter I hang on, the better it will get. Never listen to a mother's twisted logic. Nights are colder now. Nearly frigid with my desolation, I will soon get up and move on.

15. On top of the world there is a great view. Only too bad I'm not up there to see it. Ontario is coldly beautiful, wanting nothing more than to crush me beneath massive expectations.

16. Pacing, I've worn thin the heels and toes of my running shoes. Pretend it hasn't happened, isn't happening. Perhaps my desires will save us.

17. Quagmire, quarantine, quay, queen, question, quit.

18. Read between the fucking lines.

19. Soon we will all be obsolete: me, him, the mini-us who never got to see the world. She never smelled roses on a rainy day, never rode horses through gray-green forests of spruce, the sky overhead blushing with pink diamonds. She won't ever feel the sting of angry words, or the sharp pinch of hair tied too tightly. She can't ever be hurt, abducted, or abused. Should I be grateful? Should I admit that I don't know, won't ever know?

20. Tire dust and burned rubber. Tried to race from my thoughts but they caught up anyways. Tried to slice through my binds but they tied themselves back together and bled tears all over me. Tried to tell her, but she just keeps haunting me.

21. Ultrasounds lie: I was told I'd have a healthy baby girl: I even had a name picked out. Unwilling doctors had to tell me they lied, although of course they didn't put it that way.

22. Vengeance burns in my heart, the pain I wish those around me could share in and make less excruciating. Volcanoes explode in the crater in my chest, spreading their flaming ashes. Vile little mother fuckers.

23. Wasn't he supposed to be at that party? Wasn't I supposed to be at home? Well, maybe, but I was depressed and he knows what happens when I get like that. What's his excuse?

24. Xenophobia has always pissed me off. Xylophones are haunting me, taunting my ears with the sweet music she was surely going to love. Xeraphim: too many damn drugs in this world.

25. Yellow crosswalk lines are faded in the tire tracks and next to the curb. Years of age have melted the colors, blurring them into the speckled gray pavement beneath the tires. Yulia was so beautiful.

26. Zach is always too late to save me.

Naomi Day is a junior in high school in rural Massachusetts. She finds delight in dancing with an African dance and drum group on a nearby college campus, in traveling, and in reading novels about great women of the past.

Black Clock

Aimee Bender · Tom Carson · Samuel R. Delany · Don DeLillo
Brian Evenson · Janet Fitch · Rebecca Newberger Goldstein · Maureen Howard
Shelley Jackson · Heidi Julavits · Miranda July · Jonathan Lethem · Ben Marcus
Greil Marcus · Rick Moody · Geoff Nicholson · Geoffrey O'Brien
Richard Powers · Joanna Scott · Darcey Steinke · Susan Straight
Lynne Tillman · David L. Ulin · Michael Ventura · William T. Vollmann
David Foster Wallace · Carlos Ruiz Zafon

———

EDITOR Steve Erickson

subscribe online   www.blackclock.org
Published by CalArts in association with the MFA Writing Program

weave.

issue 7 available now!

jeannie paske

www.weavemagazine.net

Writing • Art • Diversity • Community